Wavelength

Pre-Intermediate • Workbook

Ben
Rowdon

with
Ana Fraile
and
Alejandro
Zarzalejos

Longman

Contents

Introduction

Welcome to the **Wavelength Pre-Intermediate Workbook**. This Workbook and the Workbook Cassette/CD are designed to be used for individual study. The sixteen Workbook units correspond to the sixteen Coursebook units, reinforcing and giving further practice of the structures and language you have studied in class. Like the Coursebook, the Workbook has a strong emphasis on natural language, set in context, and texts with a human interest element. The Workbook provides you with a variety of activities to practise structure, reading, writing, listening and pronunciation. At the end of every four units the *Do you remember?* pages help you to review and re-activate the language you have learned in those units. The tapescripts for all the listening exercises can be found in the *Answer Key* at the back of the Workbook.

Extended practice

A special feature of this Workbook is that you will find extra pages of extended practice. These pages are optional, but are designed for students who would like more challenging practice in reading and writing skills, or in the structures they have studied in the Coursebook. This extended practice takes the form of the following three sections:

Extend your reading

These sections come after every *two* units of the Workbook. They reflect the themes of the Coursebook units, but take a new look at them, use challenging texts, and include exposure to new vocabulary and structures. They are accompanied by exercises to develop your reading skills.

Extend your grammar

Do you need more grammar practice? These sections come after every *four* units of the Workbook. They include gap-fill exercises, practice in sentence transformation and use of tenses. The exercises are based on structures studied in the Coursebook.

Extend your writing

The extended writing sections also come after every *four* units of the Workbook and cover different types of writing activities such as book reviews, compositions, and formal and informal letters. Clear models are given as well as tips to help you organise your writing.

① Finding out about people

Asking questions

1 a) Fill in the gaps with *when*, *where*, *who* or *what*.

1 ......*Who*...... are you?

2 .... are you from?

3 .... 's your address?

4 .... 's your name?

5 .... do you live?

6 .... time do you go to work?

7 .... 's your job?

8 .... do you do?

9 .... do you leave the house?

10 .... were you born?

b) Look at Clive Morrison's answers. Match *two* questions from Exercise 1a) to each answer (a–e).

a) ☐1 ☐4 Clive Morrison. Call me Clive.
b) ☐ ☐ 15, St Michael's Way. In East London.
c) ☐ ☐ I'm a doctor at St Mary's Hospital in London.
d) ☐ ☐ It depends. Usually about eight o'clock every morning.
e) ☐ ☐ A small village near Newcastle.

c) Look at the rest of the interview with Clive. Fill in the gaps with the correct form of *do* or *be*.

Example: INTERVIEWER: ...*Are*... you married?
          CLIVE: Yes, I ...*am*... .

1 INTERVIEWER: What .... your wife do?

   CLIVE: She .... a doctor, too.

2 INTERVIEWER: .... you both work in the same hospital?

   CLIVE: No, we .... She works in a private clinic.

3 INTERVIEWER: .... she like her job?

   CLIVE: I .... know. I think she .... happy. Why .... you ask her?

4 INTERVIEWER: And .... you have any children?

   CLIVE: Yes. Two. Caroline .... sixteen and Ian .... ten.

Listening: Clive's family

2 a) This is the rest of the Morrison family. Clive's wife, Betty and their children – Caroline and Ian. They are talking to the interviewer.
Before you listen, who do you think said each sentence?

1 I find my job very interesting. ...*Betty*...

2 My favourite subject is politics. ....

3 They can always contact me. ....

4 His name's Pablo – he's got such a lovely voice. ....

5 All the other kids are stupid. ....

b) 🔊 (1) Now listen and check.

c) 🔊 (1) Now listen again and answer the questions.

1 What does Betty do most days?

....

2 What's she doing today?

....

3 What does Caroline want to do?

....

4 What does Ian want to do?

....

5 What's Caroline doing at the moment?

....

6 What does Ian do every evening?

....

7 What's he doing at the moment?

....

Present Simple or Present Continuous?

3 Fill in the gaps. Use the verbs in brackets in the Present Simple or the Present Continuous form.

Hi. My name's Sergei, and this is the "Let's Speak English" group.

We all (come) _come_ from different countries, and we (study) _are studying_ English in London.

Every Tuesday and Thursday we (meet) ....[1] to discuss the news in English. We usually (choose)

.............................[2] an important international story, but it all depends on what (happen) ....[3] in the news at

that moment. Of course, we (not talk) ....[4] about the news every time! At the moment, for example, we

(discuss) ....[5] work problems. Aldona (come) ....[6] from Poland. She (live) ....[7] in

Warsaw, and she's a lawyer, but here in London she (work) ....[8] in a supermarket – until next week!

Ronaldo is Brazilian. He (work) ....[9] in a bank in Rio. He (look) ....[10] for a job in London, but

there's nothing for him. It's terrible. I'm lucky. I (work).............................[11] in the school canteen, so I (eat)

.............................[12] for free every day – and my lessons are free!

Adverbs of frequency

4 Put the words into the right order to make questions and answers.
Then match the questions (1–6) to the answers (a–f).

Example: 1 = c)

1 buy / how often / a / you / newspaper / do?

How often do you buy a newspaper? ....

2 often / out / you / go / do?

....

3 twice / clean / you / teeth / do / a / your / day?

....

4 exercise / you / how often / do / do?

....

5 to / do / go / you / how / usually / work?

....

6 English / you / your / do / practise / when?

....

a) bus / often / take / I / the.

....

b) time / I / all / practise / the.

....

c) day / one / every / buy / I.

I buy one every day. ....

d) No, / often / I / out / very / don't / go.

....

e) Yes – / morning / bed / the / in / before / and.

....

f) exercise / do / ever / I / hardly.

....

Helping people

Asking for help

5 **a)** Roberto has broken his leg, which makes life a bit difficult at school. He has to ask people to help him. Match one verb and one noun to each picture, then fill in the gaps.

Verbs				
open✓	put	get	carry	stop

Nouns				
door✓	bus	coffee	tray	cushion

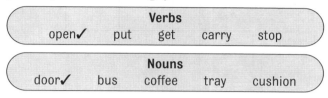

Would you mind ...*opening*..., the ......*door*......?

1

Could you .... my .... for me?

2

Can you .... me a ....?

3

Would you .... this .... under my foot?

4

Could you .... the ...., please?

Offering help

b) Lisa wants to help Roberto. How does she offer to help?

Example:

(carry / books)   Would *you like me to carry your books*?

Shall *I carry your books*?

1 (close / window)   Would ....?

2 (order / taxi)   Shall ....?

3 (get / coat)   Would ....?

4 (help you with / homework)   Shall ....

....?

5 (come and see you / Sunday)   Would ....

....?

c) Circle the correct form in these sentences.

Example: A: I like / (I would like) a coffee, please.

B: Sure. (I'll get) / I get it in a minute.

1 A: **Do you like / Would you like** me to get you a sandwich?

B: **Thank / Thanks** a lot.

2 A: **Shall I / Do I** copy these letters?

B: No, **I do it. / I'll do it.**

3 A: **I make / I'll make** some photocopies.

B: Thanks. That's really nice **of you / from you**.

4 A: **Would you like me / Shall I** to get you a coffee?

B: **Don't worry / No worry**. I'll get one later.

Vocabulary

6 a) Match each word in column A to one in column B.

Example: 1 = c)

A	B
1 current	a) skills
2 newspaper	b) design
3 intensive	c) affairs
4 professional	d) course
5 interior	e) headlines
6 computer	f) musician

b) ⊙⊙ (2) Listen and check.

c) In the words of more than one syllable in Exercise 6a), underline the stressed syllables.

Example: <u>cu</u>rrent

d) ⊙⊙ (2) Listen again and check.

Pronunciation: /iː/ or /ɪ/?

7 a) ⊙⊙ (3) Can you hear the difference between the /iː/ of sp<u>ea</u>k and the /ɪ/ of Engl<u>i</u>sh?
Listen and tick (✓) the word you hear.

Example: a) chip ☐ b) cheap ✓

1 a) ship ☐ b) sheep ☐
2 a) it ☐ b) eat ☐
3 a) bit ☐ b) beat ☐
4 a) chick ☐ b) cheek ☐
5 a) list ☐ b) least ☐

b) ⊙⊙ (4) Now listen and write the word you hear.
It is either *fit* or *feet*.

Example: *feet*

1 ....
2 ....
3 ....
4 ....
5 ....

In the office

8 a) Fill in the gaps in the sentences and then do the crossword.

| 1 | A | P | P | O | I | N | T | M | E | N | T |

1 He's got an *appointment* at twelve o'clock.

2 Oh no! The coffee .... is broken again.

3 There aren't enough windows in this ....

4 I've got a .... with Mr Johnson at 11:15.

5 Don't argue with her. She's the ....

6 This .... has only got 32 megabytes of memory!

7 When you go out, could you .... these letters for me?

8 He's the new .... – he's only here until the 15th.

9 I think I'm busy tomorrow – let me check in my ....

10 I received an .... on my computer this morning.

11 It's very .... – it <u>must</u> arrive by tomorrow!

b) Complete the question with the word in the grey boxes.

Does anybody know how to fix the .... ?

②Money matters

Past Simple

Irregular verbs

1 a) Fill in the table with the Past Simple forms of these irregular verbs.

> throw✓ catch✓ know fly bring
> teach grow buy blow think

1	...ght	2	...ew
	caught		*threw*

b) Now check your spelling. (The Irregular verb list is on page 143 of the Coursebook.)

c) 🔘🔘 (5) How do we pronounce the words in group 1? Listen and repeat.

d) 🔘🔘 (6) How do we pronounce the words in group 2? Listen and repeat.

Pronunciation: regular verbs

2 a) Look at these regular Past Simple verbs. Before you listen, tick (✓) those where we pronounce *...ed* as /ɪd/.

Examples: saved ☐
          wasted ✓
 1 finished ☐
 2 wanted ☐
 3 changed ☐
 4 decided ☐
 5 listened ☐
 6 disappeared ☐
 7 started ☐
 8 died ☐
 9 looked ☐
10 watched ☐

b) 🔘🔘 (7) Now listen and check. Then listen and repeat.

An English joke...

3 a) Circle the correct letter (a–c) each time.

Little Johnny

ⓐ came home
b) did come home
c) comed home

from school one day, and his Dad

a) did ask him,
b) asked him,
c) asked to him,

"So,

a) how went your history exam?"
b) how did go your history exam?"
c) how did your history exam go?"

... Silence ... then "Not very well,"

a) Johnny said.
b) Johnny did say.
c) Johnny sayed.

"It was too difficult! All the questions

a) was
b) were
c) did be

about things that happened before I

a) born!"
b) borned!"
c) was born!"

b) 🔘🔘 (8) Now listen and check your answers.

Money

4 Read the clues and fill in the crossword.

Across ▶

1 "Where's that money?"
   "I ... it all yesterday."

3 When he ..., he left a lot of money to his
   daughters.

6 He always does the lottery, but he never ... .

8 I know we need a new car, but we just can't ... it
   at the moment.

10 He hates me because I ... him a lot of money.

14 I can't believe you ... that waitress so much!

16 I'd love to have a big house ... an island.

17 He is not as rich ... she is.

18 I didn't have any money so I ... my car.

19 He ... me some money last week, and now he
    wants it back.

21 They must be rich – they always ... in the most
    expensive restaurants.

23 My bank manager wants to ... me tomorrow.

24 She ... all her money and land from her father.

26 I hate my job – I only work ... get money.

27 He's very ... – he often buys presents for people
    and gives money away.

Down ▼

2 Have you ... the bill?

4 Do you ... a lot of money in your job?

5 We ... 40% of our salaries last year so we can
   have a good holiday this year.

7 I usually ... in the supermarket – it's cheaper.

9 We receive a bank ... every month.

11 "..." means "*rich*".

12 You could ... the money in modern art, or a small
    business.

13 You didn't think about how to use the money well,
    you just ... it on stupid things!

15 Excuse me – how much ... this?

18 I've read this bill three times, but I ... can't
    understand it.

20 I haven't got enough money. I ... £10 more!

22 I haven't got a penny! I'm completely ... !

25 We are very happy, although we have ... money.

Used to

Positive and negative sentences

5 There's a good side and a bad side to growing older. Chris is thinking about his childhood. How was his childhood different?

Examples: Life isn't simple any more.
Life used to be simple.
I make my own decisions now.
I didn't use to make my own decisions.

1 I go to work.

....

2 I don't copy what all my friends do any more.

....

3 I feel confident with other people.

....

4 I'm not frightened of everything.

....

5 I don't believe in Father Christmas.

....

6 I worry about money these days.

....

7 I don't hate Monday mornings now.

....

8 People ask for my opinion these days.

....

9 Time passes so quickly these days.

....

10 My older brother doesn't hate me any more.

....

Used to or Past Simple?

6 a) Read this story. Sometimes you can change the Past Simple to *used to*, and sometimes you can't. Change the underlined Past Simple verbs to *used to* if it is possible.

used to love   *(no change)*
I loved her, but she left me. Now I hate her. I think.

I walked[(1)] to work through the park every day. One day,

I saw[(2)] her, near the lake, and I started[(3)] to talk to her.

After that, we met[(4)] every morning. I told[(5)] her all about

my job, and my life – she didn't answer[(6)]. She never

spoke[(7)]. I took[(8)] her everywhere with me. Once, we

went[(9)] to the Museum of Modern Art, but I don't think

she liked[(10)] it. She didn't look[(11)] at the pictures. In those

days, I woke[(12)] up every morning with a smile on my

face. But one morning, she didn't come[(13)] to the park.

The next morning she still wasn't[(14)] there. I never saw[(15)]

her again. I was[(16)] so happy, and now I'm so miserable.

You can't trust ducks, can you?

CD Reviews: comparatives

__7__ **a)** Read these two CD reviews.

 Adam by Fishmonger

(Sonya Records. $16.00)

This isn't as good as last year's *Eve*, but I still think it's a great collection of twelve excellent songs. At 71 minutes it's a little bit long, but it's never boring. It has sold nearly a million copies, and is still selling really well. Not bad for a group that started their career in 1979.

 Boot Up by Rubbish

(Disco Compacto Records. $12.95)

When Rubbish started, they were still at school. Now, two years later, they are one of Britain's favourite bands. I'll never understand how this record sold seven million copies in three months, and is still selling thousands every day. There are nineteen songs on *Boot Up* and they are all the same. Luckily they are all very short (less than 2 minutes) and the whole CD is only 37 minutes long. The strange thing is, I still found time to be bored.

b) Now use these adjectives to make comparative sentences about *Adam* and *Boot Up*.

Example: long: *"Adam" is longer than "Boot Up"*.

1 short: ....

2 expensive: ....

3 successful: ....

4 cheap: ....

5 interesting: ....

6 young: The members of ....
....

7 good: The magazine thinks ....
....

8 bad: The magazine thinks ....
....

Listening: Choosing a video

__8__ **a)** 👀 (9) Andrew and Becky are trying to decide which video to rent for the evening. Listen to their conversation. Does Andrew like or dislike 1–5?

1 the film *Casablanca*
2 Marilyn Monroe
3 the director of *Romance Again*
4 chocolate
5 the film *Night Kiss*

b) 👀 (9) Do they agree (A) or disagree (D) about items 1–5 in Exercise 8a)?

1 .... 2 .... 3 .... 4 .... 5 ....

c) 👀 (9) First try to correct the mistakes in these phrases. Then listen to the conversation again to check your corrections.

1 I don't think yes.
I don't think so.
....

2 Do you think so? I no.
....

3 I am not agree.
....

4 You joking!
....

5 So I do.
....

6 Neither I do.
....

7 I suppose that yes.
....

8 Are you agree?
....

Extend your reading Units 1–2

Are you a good dancer? Would you like to go on a luxury cruise for free?

As more and more women decide to travel independently, Blue Line, a major cruise line, offers mature single men the opportunity to work as cruise hosts. These gentlemen accompany cruise guests, acting as dance partners and general public relations representatives. They have all the benefits of a cruise guest, but none of the expenses. Would you like to be a cruise host?

Requirements
The typical cruise host is aged 45 or over. He is a good dancer and generally fit. He is also good at conversation and preferably a non-smoker.

Job description
Hosts get up early and go to bed late. They have all their meals with the rest of the passengers and take part in all the games and activities in the cruise entertainment programme. They also participate in on-shore excursions as cruise representatives. In addition, they act as dance partners for the passengers every evening.

Benefits
Cruise hosts travel as passengers, with cabin accommodation. They also eat with the rest of the guests aboard the ship and have free drinks at the bar. Our company offers round-trip air transportation to the point of departure. Hosts take part in excursions free. A cruise host receives a percentage of all tips. Above all, a cruise host gets the chance to travel the world and make new friends.

If you think you are qualified, we'd like to meet you. Call us for an interview.

**Blue Line Cruises
24 Cavendish Grove
London W1M ADB
Tel. 0171 0568 78 32**

---

1 Read the advertisement for cruise hosts. Are the sentences (1–6) true (T) or false (F)? Write T or F in the boxes.

A cruise host …
1 … is a man. ☐
2 … is very young. ☐
3 … works all day. ☐
4 … dances very well. ☐
5 … has a good salary. ☐
6 … can travel for free. ☐

2 Are these sentences true (T) or false (F)? Write T or F in the boxes.

1 Cruise lines need cruise hosts because many women travel alone. ☐
2 Cruise hosts need to be in good physical condition. ☐
3 They only work on the ship. ☐
4 All hosts get to the ship's point of departure by plane. ☐
5 Hosts get money from tips. ☐

3 Match the words (1–7) from the advertisement with their meanings (a–g) below.

1 major
2 accompany
3 accommodation
4 round-trip
5 take part in
6 get the chance to
7 qualified

a) go somewhere with someone
b) have the opportunity to
c) principal, important
d) participate in
e) rooms
f) to the place and back
g) with the necessary characteristics and training

3 It's your life!

Reading: Monica's story

1 **a)** Here are four newspaper headlines from different times in the life of Monica Gordon (Coursebook, Unit 3). Match each headline to one story in Exercise 1b).
Write the letter of the story – a), b), c) or d) – in the box next to the headline.

1 ☐ **16-Year-Old Millionaire's Daughter Joins Hippie Commune**

2 ☐ **Indian Wedding for Gordon Child**

3 ☐ **Baby Born to Hollywood Producer**

4 ☐ **"It's Over!" – Monica**

b) Now put the verbs in the boxes into the Past Simple and fill in the gaps in the articles.

be✓	tell	start	have
can (negative)	want	give	leave

a) Congratulations to film producer Sam Gordon and his wife. Their three kilo baby girl ..*was*.. born in the Sunnyview Hospital at midnight, Tuesday. Mrs Cheryl Gordon ....(1) the hospital soon afterwards, and we talked to her at her home last night. She ....(2) us that Mr Gordon wasn't with her at the birth. "He ....(3) come," she said. "He ....(4) an important business meeting." And how is the child? "Well, we ....(5) a boy. But I suppose a girl is OK." And where is the baby now? "Oh – she ....(6) to cry, so I ....(7) her to one of the servants."

want	die	move	live
inherit	get	explode	meet

c) ... and fireworks ....(1) in the sky over the beach at Panaji, as the beautiful couple promised each other eternal love. Monica (19 years old) and Brian "Che" Whimsey (21 years old) ....(2) married in India "Because we ....(3) to escape from the capitalists of Hollywood". "Che" ....(4) Monica at a hippie commune where they ....(5) for two years before they ....(6) to Mexico a year ago. "Che" ....(7) a lot of money when his father ....(8) last year, but he says, "Daddy's money isn't important. I'm still a revolutionary. Please don't print that ..."

find	need	speak	miss
get (negative)		run	

b) The teenage daughter of Hollywood's golden couple, the Gordons, has joined a commune in the hills south of San Francisco. She ....(1) away last Tuesday night, but her parents ....(2) worried until Friday, when Monica ....(3) her favourite TV programme *That's Your Hair!* This newspaper ....(4) Monica yesterday and ....(5) to her – "I ....(6) to escape," she said. "It's horrible to be rich ..."

hate	get	phone	speak
go	look	see	join

d) Monica Gordon ....(1) divorced last week from her husband of five years, Brian "Che" Whimsey. "I got so lonely!" she told us yesterday from her house in Los Angeles. "I ....(2) after the house myself! I only ....(3) to friends when I ....(4) the USA! I hardly ever ....(5) Che. He ....(6) a revolutionary group called "The Family", and just ....(7) to bars and had meetings! I ....(8) it. I'm not political."

c) Now read the articles again, and answer these questions.

1 Why wasn't Mr Gordon there at the birth?

2 Where was the hippie commune?

3 How long was Monica missing before her parents noticed?

4 How old was Monica when she moved to Mexico?

5 How old was "Che" when his father died?

6 How long were Monica and "Che" married?

Listening: An interview with Monica

2 📼 (10) **Monica talks about her divorce in an interview. Read the text, then listen to the interview. The meaning of the text and the interview are the same, but she uses *different words*. Write the words she uses in the interview.**

was very

I ~~got really~~ bored, being married to Brian. He always went out every night at nine o'clock, and sometimes he didn't return until nine the next morning. I had no-one to talk to. He said he was at political meetings, but sometimes I could smell perfume on his clothes. I think he met another woman at those meetings. But ... I don't care. Life's more exciting without him!

Pronunciation: linking

3 **a)** **Mark which words in these sentences link together.**

Example: He told_us to stop_it.

1 He missed a meeting.
2 I liked her father.
3 She wanted everything.
4 My parents bought a small house.
5 Does it make a difference?
6 She said they lived in Africa.
7 She studied economics at university.
8 I needed all the money.
9 Sometimes I think about him.
10 Listen and understand.

b) 📼 (11) **Now listen and check.**

Memories

Past Simple

4 **a)** **Complete these childhood memories with a verb from the Word Box in the Past Simple.**

| try on ✔ | cut | lock | drink | cry |
| go | break | argue | find | eat | fall |

Audrey: I *tried on* my mother's clothes.

1 Joanna: I .... to Italy with my mum and dad.

2 Charlotte: I .... off a bicycle when I was five or six.

3 Philip: I .... my brother's favourite toy car.

4 Mark: I .... my head very badly in a football game.

5 Victor: I .... because I lost my mum in a supermarket.

6 Julia: I .... myself in a wardrobe by accident.

7 Valerie: I .... paint when I was three.

8 Graham: I .... with all my teachers at school.

9 Simon: I .... some very old coins in a field.

10 Noel: I .... all my sister's birthday cake.

Remember doing

4 **b)** What do they remember doing? Look back at Exercise 4a) and complete the sentences.

Example: Audrey _remembers trying on her mother's_ _clothes._

1 Joanna ....

....

2 Charlotte ....

....

3 Philip ....

....

4 Mark ....

....

5 Victor ....

....

6 Julia ....

....

7 Valerie ....

....

8 Graham ....

....

9 Simon ....

....

10 Noel ....

....

Past Simple questions

c) Now make questions for these answers.

Example: _Where did Joanna go ?_

To Italy, with her mum and dad.

1 .... ?

His brother's favourite toy car.

2 .... ?

Because he lost his mum in a supermarket.

3 .... ?

When she was five or six.

4 .... ?

His teachers.

5 .... ?

In a field.

Pronunciation: /tuː/ or /tə/?

5 **a)** How do we pronounce *to* in these sentences? Before you listen, tick (✓) /tuː/ or /tə/.

	/tuː/	/tə/
1 I remember going to Italy.	✓	☐
2 We went to France.	☐	☐
3 He wanted to make some money.	☐	☐
4 She wanted to earn some money.	☐	☐
5 He was kind to everyone.	☐	☐
6 She was never kind to me.	☐	☐
7 They'd like to do something different.	☐	☐
8 We didn't want to eat bread and water.	☐	☐

b) 🔘🔘 (12) Now listen and check.

Multi-word verbs

6 Complete the sentences using a verb from the Word Box in the correct form.

> look at ✓   look for   bring up   fall off
> wait for   run away   talk about   listen to
> get up   go out   look after

Example: I didn't watch much TV, but I used to _look at_ picture books a lot.

1 I was .... in a small town near Oxford.

2 When my parents went out, my grandmother .... me.

3 When I was three, I .... a bicycle and cut my head.

4 My father used to hide chocolate eggs in the garden, and we had to .... them.

5 Parents never .... their children's opinions.

6 I stayed awake on Christmas Eve and .... Father Christmas.

7 I didn't .... at night until I was fourteen.

8 I had to .... early to go to school.

9 My grandmother was like a friend to me. We .... everything.

10 I tried to .... when I was four, but a police officer found me and brought me home.

Reading: Bruce Lee

7 a) Read this short biography.

The Short Life of Bruce Lee

Bruce Lee is different from other "martial arts" film stars because even people who have never seen one of his films know his name and recognise his face on the thousands of posters, T-shirts and books that are still available decades after his death. Bruce Lee is much more than the star of some 1970s Kung Fu films. His early death in 1973 has made him a Hollywood legend, like James Dean or Marilyn Monroe. An image of eternal youth, forever young and beautiful.

Bruce Lee was Chinese, but he was born in San Francisco on 27th November, 1940 (the year of the dragon), when his father – Lee Hoi Chuen – was on tour with the Cantonese Opera Company. The Lee family returned to Hong Kong the next year, but his parents sent Bruce back to the USA when he was 18, because he was always fighting with other boys in the streets.

In America, Bruce Lee divided his time between studying at school and university, and working in Chinese restaurants. But he always gave Kung Fu lessons, and in 1964 he opened his second school of Kung Fu in Oakland, California.

While Bruce was demonstrating his own method of Kung Fu (Jet Kune Do) at an international karate tournament, the producer of the popular American television series *Batman* saw him, and invited him to Los Angeles. In 1966 Lee began work on the television series *The Green Hornet* as Kato, the detective's assistant. From 1967 to 1971 he had small parts in many Hollywood productions, and gave Kung Fu lessons to many actors, including Steve McQueen. In 1971, he made his first big film – *Fists of Fury* – in Thailand. It was an enormous success, and Bruce Lee became a Hong Kong superstar. His success continued with *The Chinese Connection* and *The Way of the Dragon*. In 1973 Bruce Lee made *Enter the Dragon* – it was the first time the US and Hong Kong film industries had worked together.

Unfortunately, Bruce Lee never saw this last film, because a month before it came out, he died in Hong Kong, on 20th July, 1973. Twenty-five thousand people attended his funeral there. The following week there was a smaller funeral, in Seattle, and that is where he was buried, on July 30th. When *Enter the Dragon* opened, it was an international success, beginning the legend of Bruce Lee.

b) Write questions for these answers.

Example: *What nationality was Bruce Lee?*   Chinese.

1 .... ?   San Francisco.

2 .... ?   November 27th, 1940.

3 .... ?   Lee Hoi Chuen.

4 .... ?   Because he was always fighting.

5 .... ?   In Chinese restaurants.

6 .... ?   *Fists of Fury.*

7 .... ?   20th July, 1973.

8 .... ?   25,000.

c) Find a word or phrase which means:

1 oriental fighting sports ....

2 ten years ....

3 went back ....

4 showing ....

5 competition ....

6 helper ....

7 very big ....

8 came to (a place) ....

9 the next ....

4 Hooray for Hollywood!

Interested or interesting?

1 Mike Sprocket's new film has just come out. Read these comments about the film, and fill in the gaps with adjectives formed from the verbs in brackets.

Example: The film was quite _exciting_, but the children were a bit _frightened_ . (excite, frighten)

1 Everyone told me it was .... , but I was really .... (excite, bore)

2 The film had some .... moments. (interest)

3 I was really .... It was so different from his other films! (surprise)

4 There were one or two .... bits, but in general it was quite .... (amuse, bore)

5 I was really .... before it started, but I didn't like it. (excite)

6 The story was a bit .... , but the ending was really .... I cried! (confuse, move)

7 He doesn't usually make .... films. I hated it. (depress)

8 It was a really long film. I'm very .... (tire)

Pronunciation: /ɪz/

2 **a)** Tick (✓) the words where we pronounce final syllable /ɪz/

1 exercises	✓	6 tenses	☐
2 languages	☐	7 headlines	☐
3 bottles	☐	8 times	☐
4 courses	☐	9 sentences	☐
5 experiences	☐	10 chocolates	☐

b) **oo** (13) Listen and check.

Cinema

3 Read the clues and fill in the crossword.

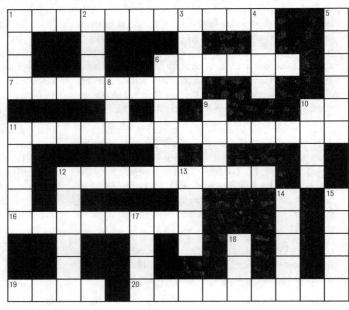

Across ▶

1 A very successful film is called a ... .
6 American actor in *Titanic* – Leonardo Di ... .
7 Alfred Hitchcock was a famous film ... .
10 "Why ... you want to be in this film?" he asked.
11 *Star Wars*, *Bladerunner* and *2001* are ... ... films.
12 The film capital of the world is ... .
16 A film which is exciting and frightening is called a ... .
19 "I had a small ... in *Titanic*," said the actress.
20 Steven ... made *ET* and *Saving Private Ryan*.

Down ▼

1 American actor in *Seven* and *Interview with a Vampire* – ... Pitt.
2 American actor in *8mm* and *Face Off* – Nicholas ... .
3 A successful and famous actor is called a ... .
4 Dustin Hoffman and Tom Cruise film: ... *Man*.
5 An ... film has a lot of fights, explosions, etc.
6 A ... is a funny film.
8 "... you ride a horse?" he asked the actress.
9 American actor in *Taxi Driver* – Robert de ... .
10 "I have ... some modelling," said the actress.
11 The ... man replaces the actor in dangerous scenes.
12 *Frankenstein*, is a ... film.
13 "... you in any films before *Titanic*?" he asked.
14 The film has a very exciting car - ... through the streets of San Francisco.
15 Stars want to look ... for as long as possible.
17 "Oh, I've been in ... of films," said the actress.
18 American actor in *The King and I* – ... Brynner.

Experiences

Present Perfect

4 **a)** Joe is a stunt man and Mel is a stunt woman. What have they done? Look at the table, then complete the sentences in the Present Perfect. Use the verbs from the Word Box.

	Joe	Mel
1 a motorbike	✓	✓
2 a fast car	✓	✓
3 a machine gun		✓
4 Africa		✓
5 a wild animal		✓
6 a mountain		✓
7 a bone	✓	✓

ride✓	use	break	climb
fight	drive	visit	

1 Both Mel and Joe *have ridden a motorbike* .

2 Both ....

3 Only Mel has ....

4 Only ....

5 ....

6 ....

7 ....

b) What hasn't Joe done?

1 He hasn't .... a machine gun.

2 He .... Africa.

3 ....

4 ....

Past Simple

c) Match Mel's experiences in Exercise 4a) with her details below. Complete the sentences in the Past Simple.

1 "I *rode* a 1200cc Harley Davidson in *Death on Wheels*."

2 "I .... Mount Everest in 1991."

3 "I .... a Ferrari six months ago."

4 "I .... Mozambique in 1998."

5 "I .... a lion when I was in Mozambique."

6 "I .... my leg two years ago."

7 "I .... an Uzi machine gun in *Police Brutality*, in 1996."

Past Simple or Present Perfect?

d) Fill in the gaps with *did(n't)*, *has(n't)*, *have(n't)* *was(n't)* or *were(n't)*.

1 **A:** .... Joe been to Africa?

 B: No, he ....

2 When .... Mel go to Mozambique?

3 **A:** .... Joe in *Death on Wheels*?

 B: No, he .... but Mel ....

4 **A:** .... Joe ever broken his leg?

 B: Yes, he ....

5 .... Mel and Joe ever worked together?

6 They .... in a film together in 1997.

7 Mel .... fight a lion in Paris.

8 How .... Mel break her leg?

9 Mel .... in *Police Brutality* in 1996.

10 **A:** .... Mel and Joe in *Titanic*?

 B: No, they ....

Superlative adjectives

5 a) Write the superlative form of these adjectives.

adjective	superlative
rich	*richest*
beautiful	*most beautiful*
tall	
expensive	
funny	
successful	
handsome	
dangerous	
good	
bad	

b) Mr Mogul is producing a huge Hollywood spectacular. He's on the phone to his assistant. Fill in each gap with a superlative from the table in Exercise 5a).

MR MOGUL: OK! Now are you listening? I want people to *love* the stars – OK? I want the guy to be a real hero! He has to be *big*! Get me the *tallest* actor in Hollywood! At least two metres tall!

And they both have to look *fantastic*! I want the ....(1) actor and the ....(2) actress you can find!

Who won the Oscar for the ....(3) actor last year? Get him! I don't care how much he costs! I

don't care if this is the ....(4) film in history! Money isn't important!

No, I don't want Tommy Tomson! He's no hero! He's never taken a risk. Taking a bus is the ....(5) thing he's ever done! Find a real man!

And I want people to *laugh*! Who is the ....(6) writer in Hollywood at the moment? OK! Get them all! And the director! Who? No I don't want him! He's terrible! *Night Kiss* was the ....(7) film I've seen in my life! Awful!

Now what is the ....(8) film of the last ten years? What's made the most money? Get me the director of *that* film!

OK, OK, we'll need lots of money! So we'll *get* lots of money! Who is the ....(9) man in Hollywood? Me? Oh ... excellent!

c) 👓 (14) Now listen and check.

6 a) Match the words on the left (1–7) with the "extreme" forms on the right (a–g).

Example: 1 = d)

1 like	a) awful
2 dislike	b) fabulous
3 bad	c) miserable
4 pretty	d) love
5 poor	e) beautiful
6 sad	f) hate
7 good	g) broke

b) Now fill in the gaps in these sentences with the correct form of the "extreme" words (a–g) from Exercise 6a).

1 That was the worst film I've ever seen. I ...*hated*... it! It was ....!

2 I'm feeling .... because I haven't got any money – I'm completely ....!

3 She's absolutely .... I think she's the best-looking woman I've ever seen.

4 Mmm! This food is great. Really .... I .... it!

Do you remember? Units 1–4

Used to

1 Bob and Ted are looking at some old school photos. Bob was always a very good student, and Ted was always very bad.

Match the verbs and phrases in the box to the correct student, and make sentences using *used to*.

> not smoke✓   listen / Walkman in class✓
> go / library   not copy from other students
> not do homework   have fights   arrive early
> not study for exams   listen / teacher   smoke

Bob	**Ted**
Bob didn't use to smoke.	*Ted used to listen to*
....	*his Walkman in class.*
....	....
....	....
....	....
....	....
....	....

Present Perfect or Past Simple?

2 Circle the correct form in these sentences.
Example: I **have seen /** (**saw**) him last week.

1 She **has started / started** work two days ago.

2 *Star Wars* is on TV tomorrow. **Did you see / Have you seen** it?

3 I love your watch. Where **did you buy / have you bought** it?

4 **Did you try / Have you tried** Chinese food before?

5 I **have never been / never went** to Mexico – I might go next year.

Present Simple or Present Continuous?

3 a) Fill in the gaps in the conversation with the Present Simple or the Present Continuous of the verbs in brackets.

JOHN: Where .....*are*....... you .....*going*.....? It's half past one in the morning! (go)

JANE: I .... anywhere. (not go)
I .... the door because it's hot in here! (open)

JOHN: So why .... you .... a coat? (wear)
You .... usually .... a coat in bed! (not wear)

JANE: Er ... erm ... I .... to the kitchen for a glass of milk. (go)
I .... a glass of milk at half past one every morning. (have)

JOHN: I .... you! (not believe)
I think you ....! (lie)

JANE: OK. It's true! I .... you! (leave)
I ....! (run away)

JOHN: Fine. But please be a bit quieter. I .... to sleep! (try)

JANE: Sorry. Bye.

b) 🔊 (15) **Now listen and check.**

Extend your reading Units 3–4

1 a) How much you know about Harrison Ford? Are these statements true (T) or false (F)? Write T or F in the boxes.

1 Harrison Ford became famous after he played the part of Indiana Jones. ☐
2 Harrison Ford didn't like *Star Wars*. ☐
3 He earns about 10 million dollars per film. ☐

b) Now read the magazine interview with Harrison Ford and check your answers.

2 Fill in the gaps in the sentences with words from the Word Box. You don't need all the words.

audience	costumes	project	audition
movie	part	career	lines

1 The clothes actors wear in films are ....

2 The people who watch a film are the ....

3 An .... is a test for a part in a film.

4 An actor's .... are the words that he learns for his part in a play or film.

5 An American word for *film* is ....

3 a) Match 1–4 to a–d to complete the expressions.

1 To play	a) a star
2 To keep	b) the opportunity to (do something)
3 To become	c) in shape
4 To have	d) a part

b) Now use the correct form of the expressions in Exercise 3a) to fill in the gaps in these sentences.

1 When I was at university I .... sing with a band; it was so much fun!

2 Sean Connery .... in an *Indiana Jones* film with Harrison Ford.

3 To .... , I go to the gym every day.

4 Most actors and actresses in the world would like to .... in Hollywood.

Interview with Harrison Ford

America is still crazy about him! Proof: a survey released in January 1999 designated him the best movie actor of all time, ahead of John Wayne.

TELE-STAR: The fact is that the only *Star Wars* actor who has become a star is you. Do you know why?

HARRISON FORD: In fact with Han Solo I had the opportunity to portray a person much more sympathetic than Luke Skywalker, portrayed by Mark Hamill. Han is a cool guy ... It's normal that he would be more pleasing to the audience than that upright, honest Luke Skywalker.

TS: What memories do you have of the filming of *Star Wars*?

HF: I used to say to myself constantly "This story is weak. It'll never work. My career is over". And it's true that I found the dialogue stupid, and my costume ridiculous. Fortunately there was George Lucas (the director). He is my best memory of the film. His determination was impressive.

TS: How did you get the role of Han Solo?

HF: I knew George Lucas after playing in his first film, *American Graffiti* in 1973... One day George called me and asked me to feed lines to an actor who was auditioning for Han Solo. I found that very insulting and told him so. Suddenly, confused, George gave me an audition for the role. And the rest is history.

TS: You have played other heroes such as Indiana Jones with great success. However, you have been a family man in your films lately ...

HF: And that pleases me. Even if I am well-preserved for my age, it would be ridiculous to persist to want to play Indiana Jones. Today, I try to play parts which are more human.

TS: A superstar with a twenty-year career, salaries of $20 million per film – what else do you want from life?

HF: To have a thirty-year career and earn $30 million per film! (*He laughs.*) Seriously, I don't want anything in particular.

Extend your grammar Units 1–4

1 Here is an extract from the novel of *Forrest Gump*, which was made into a film, starring Tom Hanks. Fill in the gaps with words from the Word Box. You don't need all the words.

> at   because   better   every   went   for
> full   good   how   it   into   later
> one   so   that   them   to   while

I was at hospital .... [1] two months. After the first few weeks my leg was getting .... [2], and one day I .... [3] down into the little town, to the fish market. I bought some shrimps, and one of the cooks at the hospital cooked them for me. Two days .... [4], I went back to the fish market and talked to a man who was selling shrimps. "Where do you get .... [5] ?" I asked him. He immediately started talking fast in a language that I couldn't understand, but he took me somewhere – past all the boats and the beach. There he took a net and put it .... [6] the water. When he took it out again, it was .... [7] of shrimps! .... [8] day for the next few weeks, I went with Mr Chi (that was his name) and watched him .... [9] he worked. He showed me .... [10] to catch shrimps with the net, and it was .... [11] easy that an idiot was able to do it! And I did .... [12]!

Then .... [13] day I got back to the hospital and a Colonel Gooch said, "Gump, we're going back .... [14] America together! You are going to see the President of the United States, and he's going to give you a medal .... [15] you are very brave."

From *Forrest Gump* by Winston Groom
(Penguin Graded Readers)

2 Complete the second sentence so that it means the same as the first sentence.

Example: There are only ten plastic cups and we need more for the party.

There aren't *as many plastic cups* as we need for the party.

1 Shall I make these photocopies for you?

Would .... make these photocopies for you?

2 Film stars usually look younger than they are.

Film stars don't usually look

.... as they are.

3 When I was in my thirties I never smoked cigars, but I do now.

When I was in my thirties .... cigars.

4 There is no-one in this class as intelligent as Julia.

Julia is .... person in this class.

5 "Yes, I put the key on my desk. I remember now," my husband said.

My husband said that he remembered

.... on his desk.

6 I am sometimes bored with my job.

I sometimes find ....

7 Could you sign this letter, please?

Would .... signing this letter, please?

8 Jack isn't as good at mathematics as Katy.

Katy .... than Jack.

Extend your writing Units 1–4

Writing a review

1 What order would you put this information if you wanted to write a review of a book?

1 A description of the main character in the novel.
2 The introduction: general ideas about the novel.
3 The conclusion: a critical impression of the novel.
4 A description of the plot.

2 Read the book review below. What order did the writer follow? Match the points (1–4) in Exercise 1 to the paragraphs (a–d) in the review.

The Job by Douglas Kennedy Little

Brown 387pp, £12.99

a) You may think that a thriller about a man who sells advertising space for a computer magazine called CompuWorld does not sound very interesting. But the author, Douglas Kennedy, really knows how to tell a story. The novel moves fast and is very entertaining.

b) The hero of the book, Ned Allen, is a top executive in New York. He makes a lot of money, but he also spends it fast. His idea of social success is to get a reservation for the most expensive restaurant in town, where he can spend the evening watching famous people. Ned is also a member of an exclusive sports club and has a luxury apartment in a fashionable area of town.

c) Everything starts to change in Ned's life when a new corporation buys CompuWorld and a new chief executive arrives. This new man soon tells our hero that he is going to fire his boss and give Ned the job. This marks the beginning of a new life for Ned ... but that is enough about the plot. I will let you read the rest yourself.

d) Although the book is not great literature, it is very exciting. The last chapter, in particular, is full of suspense. This is the kind of book you will enjoy during a summer holiday or a rainy autumn weekend. Personally, I liked it so much that I can't wait to see the film!

Writing Tip

Before you write a composition, it is a good idea to think about how to divide your work into paragraphs. Each paragraph should concentrate on one main idea.

3 Draw a table in your notebook with these four headings:

1 Type of book / film

2 Plot

3 Main character(s)

4 Personal impression

Complete the table with your ideas about a book or a film that you have read or seen recently. Make notes. Do *not* write full sentences.

4 Now write your own book or film review. Use the following notes to help you.

Introduction:
... is a thriller / comedy / drama about ...
The story is interesting / boring / exciting and / but funny / depressing / moving

Plot:
In the novel / film, a man / woman / detective ...

Characters:
The main character(s) in the novel / film is / are ...

Conclusion:
I liked / didn't like the novel / film because ...
The beginning / end / middle part is especially ...
This is a book / film for people who like ...

5 Playing by the rules

Rules and regulations

1 a) Complete the signs (1–5) using a verb from the Word Box in the correct form.

> turn down✓   smoke✓   drive   eat
> fasten   fish   park   drink

Please **turn down** your personal stereo.

No **smoking**

1 No
....

No .... or
.... in
the library.

2 Wet road. Please
.... carefully.

4 No ....

.... your seatbelt.

b) Explain the signs, using *can't* or *have to*.

Examples: You have to ..*turn down your personal stereo*.. .
You can't ..*smoke*.. .

1 You can't ....

2 You have to ....

3 ....

4 ....

5 ....

2 a) Match two phrases from the Word Box to each situation in sentences 1–5. Then complete the sentences using *have to* or *can't*.

> walk on the paths✓   pick the flowers✓
> shout at the teachers   break the speed limit
> open the window   sit down during take-off
> be quiet   obey orders
> stay in bed all day   do your homework
> drive on the left   touch the paintings

Example: In a park, you ..*can't pick the flowers*..
and you have ...*to walk on the paths*.. .

1 At school, you ....

    and you ....

2 In an art gallery, you ....

    and you ....

3 On a road in the UK, you ....

    and you ....

4 On an aeroplane, you ....

    and you ....

5 In the army, you ....

    and you ....

2 b) Use the verbs in brackets to complete these sentences. Use *can / can't, have / has to* or *don't / doesn't have to.*

1 (smoke)
In your own house you ...*can smoke*... .

On the London Underground you ....

2 (drive on the right)
In the UK, drivers ....

In France, drivers ....

3 (carry a gun)
In the UK, people ....

An American police officer ....

4 (wash / hands)
Surgeons .... their ....

before an operation.

You .... your .... with or without soap.

5 (wear a helmet)
On a motorbike, you .... in the UK.

On a skateboard, you ....,

but it's a good idea.

Pronunciation: sentence stress

3 a) Tick (✓) the sentences where the word *can / can't* is stressed.

Examples: The people can see us. ☐
I know they can. ☑

1 Can you see him? ☐
2 Yes, I can. ☐
3 I can't speak French. ☐
4 I can ride a horse. ☐
5 What languages can she speak? ☐
6 They can do what they want. ☐
7 You can't smoke in the office. ☐
8 I can. ☐
9 No, you can't. ☐
10 Can Jenny come too? ☐

b) Underline the stressed words in sentences 1–10 in Exercise 3a).

Examples: The <u>people</u> can <u>see</u> us.
I <u>know</u> they <u>can</u>.

c) 🔊 (16) Listen and check.

Listening: five conversations

4 🔊 (17) Listen to the conversations (1–5) and answer the questions. Listen as many times as you need to.

1 a) What does Johnny ask about school?

" *Why do I have to go to school?* "

b) What does the father say about work?

" *I have to go to work.* "

2 a) What does the man say about a tie?

"He ...."

b) What does the woman say about a T-shirt and jeans?

"He ...."

3 a) What does the man ask about smoking?

"Where .... ?"

b) What does the woman say about smoking?

"You ...."

4 a) What does the museum attendant say about photos?

"You ...."

b) What does the museum attendant say about the camera?

"You ...."

5 a) What does the teacher say about the homework?

"You ...."

b) What does the teacher say about this evening?

"You ...."

Make and *let*

5 Read this letter and fill the gaps with the correct form of *make* or *let*.

International Summer Camp

Dear Mummy and Daddy,

I don't like it at this camp. The counsellors don't ..._let_.... us do anything! They ....(1) us stay in the camp all the time. They don't ....(2) us swim in the lake if they aren't watching. It's stupid.
Yesterday, Andrew (my friend) and I wanted to stay awake all night, but they didn't ....(3) us. They say that tomorrow they'll ....(4) us stay up until midnight if we want to, because it's Saturday night, but usually they ....(5) us go to bed at nine o'clock!

It's worse than being at home!
Anna (our counsellor) never ....(6) us stay up late and she ....(7) us wash the plates we use when we eat! Which is stupid. And she ....(8) us wash our hands before every meal! Even breakfast! She's OK, really, but Mr Frank is horrible. He ....(9) us do a lot of running and exercising but he never ....(10) us play real games like football — only exercises like in the army.
I have to go now because we're going wind-surfing with Anna and Frank.
Love from Ian.

PS. Can I come home soon?

6 Complete this table using *can't, has to / have to, make* or *let*.

1	She can't wear jeans there.	*They don't let her wear jeans there.*
2	*He has to do what they say.*	They make him do what they say.
3	We can't make a lot of noise.	
4		They make us wear a uniform.
5	He can't use the office phone.	
6	I have to clean their cars.	
7		They make you pay before you go in.
8	The workers can't smoke in the building.	
9		They don't let her go home early on Fridays.
10		They make them get up at six o'clock every morning.
11	You have to learn Latin and Greek.	
12	I can't park in front of my house.	

Echo questions

7 Maeve is not very interested in what Derek is saying, but she's being polite. Write her questions.

DEREK: I went to Greece last month.

MAEVE: *Did you* ?

DEREK: I don't go abroad very often.

MAEVE: *Don't you* ?

DEREK: No, but I like Greece.

MAEVE: ....? (1)

DEREK: Oh yes. The people are so kind.

MAEVE: ....? (2)

DEREK: My wife's Greek, actually.

MAEVE: ....? (3)

DEREK: Yes. We visited her family.

MAEVE: ....? (4)

DEREK: Yes. In fact. She's still there.

MAEVE: ....? (5)

DEREK: Mmm. She didn't come back with me.

MAEVE: ....? (6)

DEREK: No. She doesn't want to live in England.

MAEVE: ....? (7)

DEREK: No. She hates the weather.

MAEVE: ....? (8)

DEREK: Yes. So we're going to live in Greece.

MAEVE: ....? (9)

DEREK: Yes. I'm not going to work here any more.

MAEVE: ....? (10)

DEREK: No. In fact today is my last day.

MAEVE: *Good!* ... erm ... I mean Good*bye.*

8 Match the sentences (1–12) with the responses (a–l). Then write in the appropriate echo questions for the responses (a–l).

Example: 1 = h)

1 I went to Cuba last year.

2 She was so beautiful.

3 She was ill last week.

4 We went out last night.

5 I wasn't well yesterday.

6 I don't study enough.

7 I didn't enjoy the party.

8 I think he's stupid.

9 My dad is a French teacher.

10 You look very tired.

11 They aren't going to the party.

12 She wants a new job.

a) ....? Where does he work?

b) ....? Neither do I.

c) ....? Where did you go?

d) ....? So why did you go?

e) ....? Well, I didn't sleep well last night.

f) ....? Well, I'm going. Are you?

g) ....? What was wrong with you?

h) ...... *Did you* ......? I've been there.

i) ....? How is she now?

j) ....? So do I.

k) ....? What does she want to do?

l) ....? What did she look like?

6 Where on earth?

Listening: Sweetwood

1 **a)** 🔊 (18) Listen to Alan describing a place he knows. Which picture shows Sweetwood?

a)

b)

c)

b) 🔊 (18) Now listen again and answer these questions.

1 How often did his parents take him?

2 Who did he go to Sweetwood with?

3 Why was the place *"so different"* for him?

4 What does he remember best about it?

5 When did he last go there?

c) 🔊 (18) Listen again and fill in the gaps in this part of the description.

In summer we played ....(1) games down there. ....(2), I walked round alone. I climbed up a very big ....(3) we called "The Emperor" and sat ....(4) hours, ...(5) at the sun through the leaves, or ....(6) my cousins and sister playing below. ....(7) knew I was there. ....(8) ....(9) fantastic.

Landscape

2 Put the words in the Word Box into the word map below.

trees✓   moors✓   river   cliffs
waterfall   mountains   hills   lake
beach   forests   sea

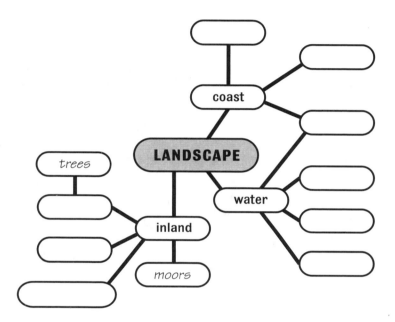

Prepositions: *in, on* or *at*?

3 Fill in the gaps in the sentences with *in, on* or *at*.

1 She lives .... San Francisco, ... the west coast.

2 The capital is .... the middle of the country.

3 My house is .... the right.

4 Newcastle is .... the north-east of England.

5 She arrived .... the airport at 6:15 p.m.

6 He went .... holiday, but she stayed .... home.

7 Marseilles is .... the south of France.

8 Marseilles is .... the south coast of France.

9 They stayed .... a hotel .... the top of a mountain.

10 The USA is .... the northern hemisphere.

Weather

Vocabulary

4 **a)** Add vowels to these words / phrases to make weather vocabulary, then put them in the correct place in the table below.

Example: fr*e* *e* z *i* ng

1 b _ _ l _ ng

2 cl _ _ dy

3 r _ _ n

4 gr _ y sk _ _ s

5 c _ ld and d_mp

6 w _ rm

7 m _ ld

8 h _ t and h _ m _ d

9 c _ _ l

10 bl _ _ sk _ _ s

Bad weather   Good weather

freezing

Listening: What's the weather like?

b) 🔘 (19) Now listen to the weather forecast. Write S (sunny), R (rain) or C (cloudy) in the circles on the map.

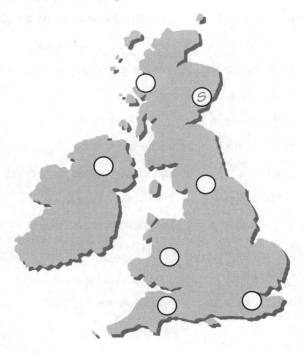

Is or *are?*

5 Fill in the gaps in the sentences with *is* or *are.*

1 The weather is OK, but there .... a lot of clouds.

2 There .... some interesting countryside around here.

3 I know a place where there .... some fantastic mountains.

4 There .... a lot of people in this country.

5 .... there a lot of snow in this part of the country?

6 I think there .... a lot of money in tourism.

7 .... there a lot of tourists in the capital?

8 There .... some incredible beaches along the coast.

9 I've seen a lake where there .... a fantastic waterfall.

10 I don't think there .... a lot of wind or rain in this area.

It is or *there is?*

6 Fill in the gaps with the correct form of *it is* or *there is.*

1 .... very windy yesterday.

2 .... a beautiful blue sky when we went to the beach.

3 "Where's the nearest pub?"

"...................... at the end of this road."

4 .... cold and damp in this country.

5 .... a lot of rain since Monday.

6 .... a train to Glasgow at 9:15 every day.

7 I think .... a bank in Peter Street.

8 The weather's awful. .... awful since the day we arrived.

9 .... freezing one day and boiling the next. I never know what to wear.

10 .... a beach about fifteen kilometres from here.

Holiday plans

7 a) Katie is asking Joanna about her holiday in Wales next week. Put Joanna's answers (a–f) in the right order, then match Katie's questions (1–6) to Joanna's answers.

Example: 1 = c)

Katie's questions

1 When are you leaving?

2 What will the weather be like?

3 Where are you going to stay?

4 How are you going to travel around?

5 Are you going to visit the capital?

6 When are you coming back?

Joanna's answers

a) no / think / I / so / don't.

....

b) 26th / come / we'll / back / probably / the /on

....

c) train / Monday / at / the / taking / 9:15 / we're /on

We're taking the train at 9:15 on Monday.

d) stay / hotels / cheap / going / we / to / are / in

....

e) probably / think / rain / it / a / will / I / lot

....

f) a / perhaps / we'll / car / rent

....

b) Read what Joanna says about her holiday. In some lines, a word is missing. In some lines there is a word which is unnecessary. Look at the examples and make the necessary corrections.

We⎰taking the train on Monday morning, and I	*..are...*
think we'll ~~to~~ arrive in Cardiff at twelve o'clock.	*...to...*
We are going stay in very cheap hotels but	...........¹
John will is taking a tent because he thinks that	...........²
we might to camp outside on one or two nights.	...........³
I have already told him that I not going to stay	...........⁴
in a tent – if he wants do it, that's fine, but	...........⁵
I am going stay in a warm bed every night.	...........⁶
I think will probably rain quite a lot, and	...........⁷
we will probably be walk for miles and miles	...........⁸
every day, so I am think it's important that we	...........⁹
to get a good night's sleep every night! Anyway,	...........¹⁰
I sure John won't want to sleep in a tent. But if	...........¹¹
he wants carry a tent around Wales for a week,	...........¹²
that's is his decision.	...........¹³

The future: *will, going to* or Present Continuous?

8 Circle the correct future form in these sentences.

Example: A: Is that the phone?

B: Oh yes. **I'm going to / (I'll)** answer it.

1 OK ... Right ... Goodbye. **I'm going to / I'll** phone you later... Yeah ... OK ... Bye!

2 She **won't pass / isn't passing** her driving test if she doesn't concentrate.

3 I can't see you tomorrow because **I'll go / I'm going** to the cinema with John.

4 Which film **are you going to / will you** see?

5 A: Tea or coffee?

B: **I'm going to / I'll** have a coffee, please.

6 The doctor says **I'm going to / I'll** have a baby.

7 A: You forgot to go to the bank!

B: Oh no! Oh well, **I'm doing / I'll do** it tomorrow.

8 The weather is so bad that the plane **will probably take off / is probably taking off** late.

Indirect questions

9 Put the words in the right order to make questions.

Example:
you / pen / do / put / where / the / remember / you?
Do you remember where you put the pen?

1 know / means / do / what / word / you / this?

....?

2 tell / she / me / can / you / where / works?

....?

3 is / do / bank / you / the / if / know / open?

....?

4 me / name / her / could / tell / you / what / is?

....?

5 remember / the / do / where / car / you / is?

....?

6 me / could / this / tell / London / to / if / is / train / you / the?

....?

7 me / can / costs / tell / how / much / you / this?

....?

8 train / do / when / the / you / leaves / know?

....?

10 Match the beginnings of the questions (1–8) to the endings (a–h).

Example: 1 = g)

1 Could you tell me when	a) does she live?
2 Excuse me. When	b) does this word mean?
3 Where	c) that is John's car?
4 Do you know where	d) does the train leave?
5 Do you know if	e) she lives?
6 Excuse me. Is	f) this word means?
7 Can you tell me what	g) the train leaves?
8 What	h) that John's car?

Listening: directions

11 ⚫⚫ (20) Listen to Paul asking for directions. Look at the map and write the correct number next to the name of his destination (a–e). (Paul always asks for directions at the station).

a) the bank ☐
b) the post office ☐
c) the nearest pub ☐
d) the travel agent's ☐
e) the hospital ☐

What is building "X"? ....

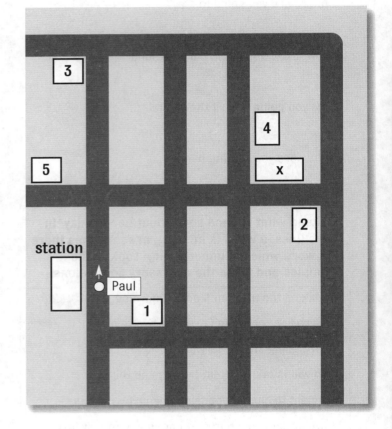

Extend your reading Units 5–6

1 a) Before you read test your knowledge of Java. Are 1–4 true (T) or false (F)? Write T or F in the boxes.

1 The beaches are the most interesting part of Java. ☐
2 You can find lions and giraffes in Java. ☐

3 The main religion in Java is Islam. ☐
4 Java is famous for the dancers who make batik clothes. ☐

b) Now read the article and check your answers.

The Mystique of Java

Jakarta
Ujung Kulon Wildlife Park
Yogyakarta
Merun Betiri Reserve

_____ (1) Indonesia's most populous island is one of the world's three or four most fascinating places. Java has the ocean and a few good places like Pangandaran where you can enjoy the beach. But the truth is that the island's cultures are focused inland – on the mountains – and not on the ocean.

_____ (2) A visit to this volcanic mountain will make it easy to understand why … Sunrise at the crater has become something of an unforgettable tourist ritual. There are also legends that include stories of human sacrifice to the gods there.

_____ (3) The last 50 or so of Java's rhinos live in the Ujung Kulon Wildlife Park. The park, on the south-western tip of Java, is Indonesia's best wildlife reserve. It might be difficult to see the rhinos, but the park offers a lot more: mouse deer, macaques, gibbons, Indonesia's wild ox, sea eagles and numerous smaller birds. Another good park is the Merun Betiri Reserve. It is home to about 150 Javan Tigers.

_____ (4) Indonesia has more Muslims than any other country on earth. Yet, it is here on Java that we find the largest Buddhist Temple in the world. The performance of the Hindu epic poem, the *Ramayana*, is an integral part of Javanese culture. It is performed as a ballet daily in Yogyakarta, the centre of Javanese culture.

The city offers some good beaches and a few other natural attractions. But what gives its personality to Yogyakarta is the culture. You can visit the Museum of East Java in Yogyakarta where there are also workshops on Javanese culture. Students in the programme can learn classical dance, the art of making batik cloth, how to dress in a truly Javanese manner, and other aspects of the culture.

Indonesia is one of my favourite places on earth. There is more to it than its beaches and the sun. Plan a trip there and enjoy its nature reserves and wonderful culture.

2 The first sentences of the first four paragraphs are missing from the article. Read the missing sentences (A–D) below. Where do they go?

A) If you want to enjoy all the beauty of Java, you shouldn't miss a safari through one of the island's nature reserves.

B) Whether you are looking for history or beaches, shopping or a profoundly cross-cultural experience, Java has it.

C) But it is the history of Java and the complexities of its culture which give the island its mystique and attractions.

D) Mount Bromo is the most popular and well known of East Java's tourist attractions.

3 Choose the correct ending to these sentences:

1 Mount Bromo is …
   a) a volcano and it is a most beautiful sight in the early morning.
   b) a nature reserve with lots of animals.
   c) a place where people go to see rituals.

2 We know that Buddhism is important in Java, because …
   a) there is a religious Buddhist dance.
   b) the majority of the people are Buddhists.
   c) there is a very important temple.

3 The *Ramayana* is …
   a) a group of dancers.
   b) a poem performed by dancers.
   c) a theatre.

7 The cruel heart

First Conditional

1 a) Match the pairs of verbs in the Word Box to the pictures (a–e).

> not sign / kill you `a` not slow down / crash ☐
> not find the formula / go crazy ☐
> come closer / scream ☐ not marry me / jump ☐

a)

If you
don't sign,
I'll kill you.

b)

If you don't
........................, I'll
.... !

c)

If you
........................, we
.... !

d)

If I ....
........................,
I .... !

e)

If you
........................, I
.... !

b) Now use the verbs from Exercise 1a) to complete what the people in the pictures are saying.

c) Now read the next part of the conversations (a–e) from Exercise 1a). Fill in the gaps, using the verbs in brackets.

Picture a: "...*Will*... you ..*leave*.. me alone if I

........*sign*........ the contract?"

(leave, sign)

Picture b: "OK! OK! I .... you if you

.... back inside! Please!"

(marry, come)

Picture c: "Yeah, well, if we .... , I

promise I .... ever again!"

(crash, not drink)

Picture d: "But if I .... the formula, I

.... the most powerful man in

the world! Ha Ha Ha!" (find, be)

Picture e: "Go on. If you .... , nobody

.... you!" (scream, hear)

d) Now look again at the pictures (a–e), and complete these questions and answers.

Example:

Picture a: What ..*will happen*.... if the man ..*doesn't sign*.. ?

The gangster .*will kill*. him.

Picture b: What will happen if she .... him?

He will jump.

Picture c: What .... happen if she

........................?

They'll crash.

Picture d: What .... if he .... the

formula?

.... crazy.

Picture e: What .... if he .... ?

....

Pronunciation: Sentence stress

2 **a)** Underline the stressed words in these sentences.

Example: If you <u>need</u> <u>help</u>, I'll <u>help</u> you.

1 If we need advice, we'll ring you.
2 If you don't know, I'll tell you.
3 If you ask Steve, he'll explain it.
4 If you want money, I'll give you some.

b) Underline the stressed words in these questions.

Example: Will she <u>come</u> if I <u>ask</u> her?

1 Will they work if he pays them?
2 Will you go if I help you?
3 Will she understand if he tells her?
4 Will he pass if he works hard?

c) 🔊 (21) Now listen and check.

Every-, some-, any-, no-

3 **a)** Fill in the gaps in the dialogues with *every- some-*, *any-*, or *no-*.

1 **THIEF 1:** Listen! I think there's ....one in the next room.

THIEF 2: That's impossible. There isn't ....one in the building at this time of night.

THIEF 1: OK. But I'm sure I heard ....thing.

2 **PATIENT:** You must give me ....thing for this cold, doctor!

DOCTOR: But I have tried ....thing! I can't think of ....thing new to give you!

PATIENT: In that case, I will have to go ....where else!

3 **TEACHER 1:** I taught that student ....thing he knows!

TEACHER 2: But that student doesn't know ....thing!

TEACHER 1: I know, I'm a terrible teacher! ....one listens to me.

4 **GIRL 1:** I'm going to the kitchen. Does ....one want a cup of tea?

GIRL 2: No. I don't want ....thing, thanks.

GIRL 3: Well, I'd like ....thing cold to drink.

GIRL 1: I'll look in the fridge. Maybe there's ....thing in there.

5 **FATHER:** Where did you go last night?

DAUGHTER: I didn't go ....where. I went to bed, because there was ....thing good on TV.

FATHER: Really? Well, ...one told me they saw you at *Jimmy's* nightclub.

DAUGHTER: That's impossible. I was at *Frankie's* – I mean ... erm ...

b) Look at the example – both sentences have the same meaning. Now complete the rest of the table.

Example: There aren't any trees in the park.	*There are no trees in the park.*
1 There isn't any money in this business.	
2	He took no risks.
3 We didn't meet any interesting people.	
4	John speaks no French at all.
5 They didn't have any problems.	
6	I have heard no news since Sunday.
7 She isn't making any progress.	

Prepositions

Multi-word verbs

4 a) Fill in the gaps in the sentences with the correct forms of verbs from the Word Box.

> break down✓   pay back   fill in   look after
> get up   pick up   travel around   grow up   think of

Example: Our car _broke down_ just before we went on holiday.

1 Before you land, you have to .... your landing card.

2 We hired a car so we could .... on our own.

3 Did you .... that book that I left on the table?

4 She .... in a small house full of children and noise.

5 What do you .... his idea?

6 I lent him a hundred dollars last year, and he never .... me ....

7 Can you .... my cats and plants while I'm on holiday?

8 I .... at 6:30 and had a shower.

Phrases with prepositions

b) Complete the phrases (a–g) with a preposition from the Word Box.

> off✓   through   on   of   in   at   to

a) a day _off_

b) .... the moment

c) That's nice .... you.

d) next .... me

e) halfway ....

f) low .... calories

g) .... my own

Now complete the sentences (1–7), using the phrases (a–g).

1 I didn't come to work yesterday. I took _a day off_ .

2 The film was so boring that I left ....

3 .... Thanks very much.

4 Come here and sit ....

5 I want to find some chocolate that's ....

6 Sometimes I just need to be ....

7 I'm working in a shop .... , but I want to leave.

Adjectives

5 a) In the Word Square, find five adjectives connected with *people*, and five with *food*. Adjectives can go down, across or diagonally ↓ → ↘ ↗.

S	N	J	E	A	L	O	U	S	D
R	U	H	A	N	D	S	O	M	E
U	R	C	P	S	Y	K	S	A	L
T	A	H	C	Z	O	F	O	G	I
H	B	E	Z	E	R	R	O	Y	C
L	M	I	J	I	S	E	T	V	I
E	F	A	M	O	U	S	W	Y	O
S	R	O	B	G	A	H	F	M	U
S	E	K	F	T	R	L	E	U	S
F	A	T	T	E	N	I	N	G	L

b) Use the adjectives from the Word Square to complete the sentences.

Food

1 I love ice cream, but it's really _ a _ _ en _ _ _ .

2 Tropico is a new kind of f _ _ _ _ drink with natural ingredients.

3 Mmmmmmm! This is absolutely _ _ _ ic _ _ _ _ .

4 This milk doesn't smell very _ _ e _ _.

5 The soup's quite _ _ _ _ y but it needs a bit more salt.

People

1 He looks like a film star. He's so _ _ n _ _ o_ _.

2 She made ten million dollars before she was twenty-five . She's been really _ _ _ _ e _ _ f _ _.

3 He's so _ e _ _ o _ _ of his wife that he won't even let her talk to the postman.

4 He's completely _ _ _ h _ _ _ _ . He'll do anything to get what he wants.

5 She's really _ _ m _ _ _ . Everybody knows who she is.

Reading: Four products that changed our lives

6 **a)** Look at these 20th century products. How old do you think they are? Try to guess.

1 The shopping trolley
☑ 19.........

2 The vacuum cleaner
☐ 19.........

3 Sliced bread
☐ 19.........

4 The motor scooter
☐ 19.........

b) Now read the four paragraphs below. Match each paragraph (a–d) to one of the products above. Then complete the dates for each one.

a) In the early days, inventor Hubert Cecil Booth took his enormous cleaning machine – on wheels – around the streets, looking for customers. When he found one, he put a long tube through the window of the house, and collected the dirt in the vacuum machine outside. It made so much noise that it frightened horses! Booth used it to clean the carpet at the coronation of King Edward VII in 1901. The king was very impressed, and ordered two models – one for Buckingham Palace, and one for Windsor Castle. After that, the machines became very popular.

b) Originally, it didn't have a seat. The rider stood on a platform – like a skateboard! It was called an Auto-Ped and the fastest it could go was 56 km per hour. Several companies tried to produce a small, practical, economical kind of motorbike, but it was the Italian company Piaggio who made the first successful scooter in 1935.

c) It was Otto Frederick Rohwedder who had this simple but brilliant idea. He introduced it in a bakery in Battle Creek, Michigan, in 1928. Only five years later 80% of the bread sold in America was already sliced and ready to eat.

d) This was not introduced by a supermarket chain, but by Sylvan Goldman, the manager of the Humpty Dumpty supermarket in Oklahoma City, USA, in 1937. He thought that if his customers had enormous baskets on wheels, they would buy more things. He was right – they bought double the quantity!

c) Now answer these questions.

1 Which products were European?

2 Which were very different from their final form?

3 Find a word which means:

a) people who buy things (noun) ....

b) very big (adjective) ....

c) an area you stand on (noun) ....

d) cheap to use (adjective) ....

e) a place that makes bread (noun) ....

f) cut (adjective) ....

g) group of shops with the same name (noun) ....

h) a container you carry for shopping (noun) ....

d) Are these sentences true (T) or false (F)? Write T or F in the boxes.

1 The first vacuum cleaner was very noisy. ☐
2 The Auto-Ped could not go faster than 56 km per hour. ☐
3 In 1928 most bread sold in the USA was sliced bread. ☐
4 Sylvan Goldman worked for a supermarket chain. ☐
5 People bought more with a shopping trolley. ☐

Pronunciation: word stress

7 **a)** Underline the stressed syllables in these words.
Example: <u>i</u>nteresting.

1 advert
2 advertisement
3 advertise
4 advertising
5 television

6 magazine
7 newspaper
8 consumer
9 customer
10 product

b) 🔊 (22) Now listen and check.

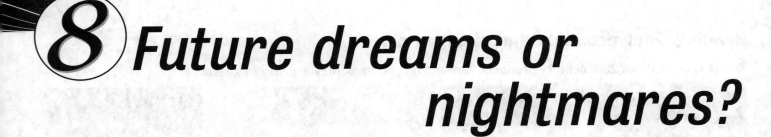

8 Future dreams or nightmares?

Future predictions: *will* and *might*

1 a) Richard and Nick have opened an ice cream stall in the middle of winter. Richard is confident it will be a success. Nick is sure it won't be. Fill in the gaps with verbs from the Word Box, using *will* or *won't*.

| start✔ | be (x3) | buy (x2) | make (x2) | rain |
| destroy | have | sell | want | |

RICHARD: Well! It's nine o'clock. The customers *will start* to arrive soon!

NICK: Rubbish! We ....[1] any money this month! "Ice Creams at Christmas"! What a stupid idea! This business ....[2] both of us!

RICHARD: Now don't be so negative! I think we ....[3] a really good month. I feel it! Everyone ....[4] to have a delicious ice cream. We ....[5] rich!

NICK: But it always rains at this time of year, and it ....[6] all this month. You'll see! And no-one ....[7] an ice cream when it's raining.

RICHARD: Well. I feel sure that this year ....[8] better than last year. I think we ....[9] hundreds of ice creams!

NICK: Of course this year ....[10] better than last year. We sold *no* ice creams last year! If we sell *one* ice cream, we ....[11] more money than last year.

RICHARD: OK!

NICK: OK what?

RICHARD: OK, I ....[12] an ice cream. Just to make you happy.

b) Miserable Nick is still complaining. Put the words in his sentences into the right order.

Example: money / probably / us / won't / any / the / bank / lend
The bank probably won't lend us any money.

1 very / next year / probably / poor / be / will / we

....

2 won't / any / we / sell / ice creams / probably

....

3 lose / our / we / all / might / money

....

4 not / tonight / we / eat / might

....

5 we'll / unemployed / I'm / be / next month / sure

....

Pronunciation: First Conditional

2 **(oo)** (23) There are two main stresses in each sentence, on the negative auxiliary verbs. Listen to the rhythm and repeat.

1 If you don't listen, you won't understand.
2 If she doesn't try, she won't win.
3 If you haven't got time, then we won't have the meeting.
4 You won't succeed if you don't try.
5 I can't explain if you won't let me.

Listening: A vision of the future

3 a) 🔲 (24) **How will the world be different in the future? Listen to four people giving their views. Listen once and answer these two questions.**

1 Are they generally optimistic or pessimistic? Tick (✓) the right answer for each person.

	optimistic	pessimistic
Moira		
Paul		
Laura		
Dan		

2 What do they think people want?

MOIRA: People just want ....

PAUL: People want ....

LAURA: People just want ....

DAN: People want ....

b) 🔲 (24) **Listen again and answer these questions.**

1 Which people talk mainly about everyday life?

....

2 Which people talk mainly about technology?

....

3 Who thinks the government will have less power?

....

4 Who thinks it will have more power?

....

5 Who thinks there will be more divorces?

....

6 Who thinks people will stop talking to each other?

....

7 Who thinks people will talk more?

....

8 Who talks about street violence?

....

9 Who talks about schools?

....

10 Which of these subjects is *not* mentioned?

clothes	war	the telephone
food	peace	video games
education	parents	money
children	films	transport
drugs	politicians	computers

c) 🔲 (24) **Now listen again to the first part of each person's opinion, and fill in the gaps.**

MOIRA: I know there are ....
problems in the world, and it's not perfect, but I
think things are .... now than they were
hundreds of years ...., and I really believe
that things will get better in ....

PAUL: Well. I think Moira's ideas are ...., and I
.... that some people are fed up with war
all the time and violence in ....,
but I can't see that the situation will get better.

LAURA: Well I think you can forget literature. ....
reads any more. People just ....
.... or get their information from the
Internet. In fact, ... don't want
information!

DAN: Well, no, frankly. I mean more ....
.... buying books now than ever before.
People are reading ...., ...
.... You have to read to use the Internet.

Adverbs and adjectives

4 a) Look at the adjectives in the Word Box. Are their adverbs regular or irregular? Write the adverbs in the table.

> dangerous✓   good   bad   fast
> slow   happy   hard   careful

Regular	Irregular
dangerously	

b) Now fill in the gaps in these sentences with adverbs from the table in Exercise 4a).

1 A: He's a good student. He really works *hard* .

  B: I know. He's excellent. He'll do very

  .... in the exams.

2 This glass bowl cost a lot of money. Carry it

  .... Don't drop it.

3 He does everything so .... It takes him

  an hour to wash his face.

4 She was smiling .... as she read the

  letter.

5 A: Steve drives so ....! Never less than

   100 kmh!

  B: I know. But he's careful – he doesn't drive

   ....

6 The teacher sent him out of the class for behaving so

  ....

c) Circle the correct form in these sentences.

Example: I feel (awful)/ awfully.

     I think the chicken I ate was (bad)/ badly.

1 He speaks so **quick / quickly** that his lessons are not

  very **easy / easily** to understand.

2 He looks very **calm / calmly**, but I know he's really

  nervous / nervously.

3 The weather was really **cold / coldly**, but she waited

  patient / patiently for the bus.

4 Only one person here works **efficient / efficiently** –

  the rest of you are too **slow / slowly**.

5 John's very **quiet / quietly** because he feels very

  angry / angrily about the whole thing.

5 a) Take the adjectives and adverbs out of these sentences.

Example: The ~~young~~ woman drove ~~carefully and well~~.

1 The thin old man walked slowly and carefully

  towards the mysterious parked car.

2 Jane ran desperately after the tiny little dog.

3 They spent two long and tiring weeks crossing the

  boiling sands of the empty desert, trying

  hopelessly to find some small sign of civilisation.

b) Without using a dictionary, try to take the adverbs and adjectives out of this paragraph, then answer the questions. Remember – without using a dictionary!

The beautiful young woman closed her tired, blue eyes and waited silently for a moment outside the tall ugly office building. At exactly ten to one she walked stiffly to the south-east entrance of the old Victorian railway station. She took a dirty broken mirror from her brown leather handbag and looked intensely at her calm, angry face. When she put the mirror back, she felt the cold, hard metal of the small gun in the bag. She walked quickly to Platform Five where she could see the tall handsome man who she knew was Mr James. She took the tiny silver gun slowly from her handbag ...

1 Where was the woman at the beginning of the
  paragraph?
2 Where was she at the end?
3 How did she get there? (by car? by plane? on foot?)
4 Who did she see?
5 What did she want to do?

That is *all* the *important* information.
If you are interested in any of the words you didn't
know, look them up in a dictionary, but remember,
they are *extra* information only.

Do you remember? Units 5–8

Adjectives

1 a) Match the two halves of these adjectives. The beginnings are on the left and the endings on the right.

self-	eleg-	pessi-	-ant	-ant	-ful	-ful
exo-	truth-	change-	-able	-ish	-tic	-tic
aw-	pleas-	opti-	-mistic	-mistic		
drama-						

b) Now fill in the gaps in these sentences with the adjectives from Exercise 1a).

1 The weather in this part of the country is very

.*changeable*.

2 Don't be so .... – you never think about

anyone else.

3 She always dresses very well – she's very

....

4 He depresses me – he's always so ....

5 I like a person who is honest and ....

6 That film was terrible – absolutely ....!

7 I like to visit countries that are romantic and a bit

....

8 The story was very .... – lots of things

happening all the time.

9 You should try to be more .... – look on

the bright side.

10 Thank you for a very .... evening.

Indirect questions

2 You are at a party. You don't know anyone. Make these questions more polite by changing them to indirect questions.

Example: Where's the toilet?
Do you know where .*the toilet is*.?

1 Where can I put my coat?

Could you tell me where ....?

2 Is there any more wine?

Do you know if ....?

3 Who is that man?

Do you know ....?

4 What's the time?

Could you tell me ....?

5 Is someone sitting here?

Do you know ....?

Find the mistake

3 Correct these sentences.

Example: Please let me ~~speaking~~! *speak*

1 If I will see him, I'll tell him.

2 Always he arrives late.

3 **A:** I don't like studying English.

  B: Neither am I – it's too difficult.

4 Please don't talk so quick – I can't understand you.

5 Every week my parents make me to clean my room.

6 She has been never to Italy.

7 **A:** What does she like?

  B: She's very friendly – I like her.

8 If he passes the exam, I am very surprised.

9 They won't let me to do what I want!

10 He drove so fastly that I felt terrible.

11 Can you tell me where is Oxford Street?

12 There are no rules in my office – we can to wear

anything we like.

Don't have or *haven't*?

4 Fill in the gaps with *don't have* or *haven't*.

1 I .... got enough money for a taxi.

2 It's not true – you .... been to Mexico.

3 They .... to stay if they don't want to.

4 You .... to decide yet – tell me next week.

5 Sorry – I .... got any idea where John is.

6 He isn't your boss. You .... to do what

he says.

Extend your reading Units 7–8

The Independent Television Commission

The ITC, the Independent Television Commission, regulates commercial television in the UK. They make rules for everything: the content of programmes and advertising, the appropriate times to broadcast certain materials, the technical quality of transmissions, etc. If broadcasters don't follow ITC rules, they are penalised.

The Independent Television Commission investigates complaints from the audience and publishes the results regularly. Here are some examples:

Section One: ....
Three viewers complained about an advertisement for a famous fried chicken restaurant. They said it gave the impression that you received more than three pieces of chicken when you ordered chicken strips and that the container with sauce in the advert was larger than the one they sold in the restaurant.

The ITC decided that the visual content of the advert clearly gave the wrong impression. As a result, the advertiser had to remove the image of the sauce container and add a title saying "3 for £2.15".

Section Two: ....
This programme showed professional performers taking extraordinary risks. Once a performer ate light bulbs in front of the camera. Six viewers complained that the programme might encourage children to do the same thing.

The ITC considered that the act was clearly presented as something very dangerous and not as something that children should do themselves. Consequently, the ITC decided that there was nothing illegal about the programme.

1 Read the first two paragraphs in the article and choose the best definition (a–c) of the ITC.

The ITC is an organisation that ...
a) creates TV programmes and advertising under certain rules.
b) punishes broadcasters when they don't follow the rules.
c) regulates TV and makes sure that broadcasters follow the rules.

2 Choose a title for Section One and Section Two from the list below.

Put More Sauce In It
Don't Try This At Home
Chicken Strips
Risky (and Illegal) Business

3 Read the text again. Are these statements true (T) or false (F)? Write T or F in the boxes.

1 The ITC decides the appropriate time to show violent films. ☐
2 The ITC keeps its decisions secret. ☐
3 The TV advert for the chicken strips showed more food than you actually got in the restaurant. ☐
4 The advertiser for the chicken restaurant only had to change a few things in the TV advert. ☐
5 The ITC penalised the broadcasters of the programme described in Section Two. ☐

4 Match the verbs in column A (1–3) to the words in column B (a–c) to make three expressions which appear in the article.

A	B
1 give	a) risks
2 make	b) rules
3 take	c) the wrong impression

Extend your grammar Units 5–8

1 Complete the second sentence so that it means the same as the first sentence.

Example: It's probable that Kevin will do well in his exams.

Kevin will ..*will probably*.. do well in his exams.

1 There wasn't anyone who could help me.

There was .... help me.

2 Julie's boss made her clean the office every day.

Julie .... clean the office every day.

3 In some parts of the USA young people can't drink alcohol before they are twenty-one.

In some parts of the USA they don't

.... alcohol before they are twenty-one.

4 My plan for my next holiday is to go to the beach.

For my next holiday I'm .... the beach.

5 You have to arrive on time for class.

You .... late for class.

6 When are you going to send these letters?

Could you tell .... send these letters?

7 Work harder or you'll never get promotion.

If you don't .... never get promotion.

8 He really is a dangerous driver.

He drives really ....

2 Fill in the gaps with *in*, *on*, *of*, *from* or *for*.

SHEILA: Do you remember the total eclipse of the sun .... [1] August 1999? Did you see it?

ANNA: Yes, I did. I was .... [2] Penzance, ... [3] Cornwall, ... [4] the south-west coast .... [5] England. It was the best place to see it; it got dark .... [6] the middle of the day .... [7] a couple of minutes. It was brilliant!

SHEILA: Yes, I know. I saw Cornwall .... [8] TV. But I was .... [9] holiday .... [10] the south-east of Spain and you couldn't see it so well .... [11] there.

ANNA: I'm sorry you couldn't see it very well. It was a once-in-a-lifetime experience. I was so excited!

3 Complete the conversation using the correct form of the verbs in brackets.

KEITH: .... [1] (ever / try) Indian food?

PAT: Yes, I have. I .... [2] (try) it once, and I didn't like it at all.

KEITH: Didn't you? Why? I love it.

PAT: I didn't really know what I .... [3] (eat) with all those sauces. Also, it was also too hot and spicy for me.

KEITH: Did you actually try the food?

PAT: Well, not really. The look and smell .... [4] (be) so different that I couldn't even .... [5] (take) a bite.

KEITH: I see. And you say you are always open to new experiences, right?

PAT: Yes, I am. I always enjoy .... [6] (try) new things.

KEITH: Sure.

8

Extend your writing Units 5–8

Introductions and conclusions

1 Read this text about boarding schools. What does each paragraph talk about?

It is true that there are some disadvantages to a boarding school. First, you can't watch as much TV as you like and you have to go to bed at a fixed time. The first few days you feel strange because you don't have all your things around you and, of course, your parents are not there. Finally, the food can be terrible some days, and you can't ask your mum to cook something different just for you.

In contrast, there are many advantages to going to a boarding school. First, there are always a lot of friends around, day and night, so it is easy to have fun. You can also use your time in a different way. For example, sometimes we play in the afternoon and have classes after that. This is especially good in winter when the days are short. Finally, I think it is good for your education because you can concentrate better on your studies and work with other children all the time.

Writing Tip

Introductions inform the reader of the general content of the composition. They need to be interesting to catch the reader's attention.

2 Choose a good introduction for the text in Exercise 1 from the introductions (1–3) below.

1 Most people think that going to a boarding school must be sad and lonely ... well, it's not. There are many things about a boarding school that can make a child very happy.

2 As you probably know, there are many advantages and disadvantages to boarding schools. Here is a description of some of them.

3 I really like my school. I am very happy that my parents chose it for me. It is like a small world where many things, even mysterious things, can happen.

3 Now choose a good conclusion (1–3) for the text.

1 In conclusion, there are many advantages and disadvantages to attending a boarding school.

2 To sum up, there are some disadvantages to attending a boarding school because you can't watch TV a lot, you have to go to bed early and the food is not very good. There are also advantages because you can make a lot of friends and study a lot.

3 I have now finished my studies at a boarding school and it has been a fantastic experience. I have often missed my family and my mum's cooking, but I feel I am well prepared for university and I have made many friendships that will last forever.

Writing Tip

The last paragraph in a composition should include a logical conclusion based on what the writer has said before, but not repeat all the arguments.

4 Now write a composition about the place where you work or study. Use the following structures to help you when you write the composition.

Introduction:
I work / study at ...
Most people think that working / studying at ... is interesting / boring / good for ... -ing.
I agree / I disagree ...

Advantages:
The main advantages to working / studying at ... are ...
There are many advantages to working / studying at ...
First, ... Then, ... Finally, ...

Disadvantages:
The main disadvantages to working / studying at ...
There are also advantages to working / studying at ...

Conclusion:
There are some advantages / disadvantages to working / studying at ... but I think that ...
It is a good experience / idea to work / study at ... because ...
Personally, I want to ... / I'm going to ...

9 My place

Adjectives

1 Make the words on the left into adjectives by using the endings on the right.
Then fill in the gaps in the sentences with the adjectives.

| welcom(e)✓ | comfort | tradition | -ing✓ | -al | -ful |
| colour | relax | friend | -ly | -ing | -able |

1 I always feel like part of the family in their house – the atmosphere is so __welcoming__ and ....

2 There's nothing unusual or modern here – all the furniture is very ....

3 I love this sofa – it's old, but it's so ....

4 The room was full of reds, blues and greens... really ....

5 I find this room very .... – I feel I could just close my eyes and start to dream...

Listening: Something special

2 **a)** 〇〇 (25) Listen to four people talking about some of their favourite things, and look at the pictures (a–h).
Match the things to the people and write a letter next to each name in the table.
How long have they had these things?

		How long?
Shirley	☐	_Since she was a student._
David	☐	....
Susan	☐	....
Ruben	☐	....

b) 〇〇 (25) Now listen to the beginning of each interview again and fill in the gaps in these sentences.

SHIRLEY: I don't .... it's the .... one of its kind in the .... , and ...

DAVID: It sounds .... , but I really .... that it brings me .... !

SUSAN: This reminds .... of my first .... to the States when I .... twelve.

RUBEN: I .... think "I must throw this .... ," but I .... do!

c) 〇〇 (25) Now listen again. Each person uses the *opposite* of the adjectives below. What are the adjectives they use in the interviews?

1 SHIRLEY: short ....   serious ....

2 DAVID: poor ....   light ....

3 SUSAN: awful ....   comfortable ....

4 RUBEN: terrible ....   cheap ....

9

Present Perfect

How long ... ?

3 Read the sentences and complete the questions, using the words in brackets.

Example: A: This is my favourite watch.
B: How long *..have you had.* it? (you / have)

1 A: I know Jim very well.

B: Really? How long .... him ? (you / know)

2 A: Joe is a member of the team.

B: Oh yes? How long .... a member? (he / be)

3 A: Jason lives in New York, you know!

B: Really? How long .... there? (he / live)

4 A: Virginia can't come. She's ill.

B: Oh no! How long .... ill? (she / be)

5 A: They work for IBM.

B: Wow! How long .... for them? (they / work)

For or since?

4 Look at the list of time expressions (1–14).
Do we use them with *for* or *since*? Complete the table.

1 two days	8 last summer
2 yesterday	9 my father died
3 a week	10 all his life
4 then	11 I was born
5 ages	12 the first six months
6 1903	13 three years
7 a long time	14 April

for...	since ...
two days	*yesterday*

5 Read the information and make sentences using the Present Perfect.

Example: Pete works for IBM. He started three years ago.
Pete has worked for IBM for three years.

1 Jason lives in New York. He moved there six months ago.

....

2 They are married. They got married in 1991.

....

3 Steve and Sarah know each other. They met ten years ago.

....

4 Betty has a dog. She bought it in 1998.

....

5 They are vegetarians. They became vegetarians in 1991.

....

6 Joe studies French. He began two months ago.

....

Present Perfect or Past Simple?

6 ◉◉ (26) Listen and tick (✓) the phrase you hear.

Example: a) He's worked hard. ☐
b) He worked hard. ✓

1 a) We've lived there for a year. ☐
b) We lived there for a year. ☐

2 a) She's walked for miles. ☐
b) She walked for miles. ☐

3 a) They've changed their money. ☐
b) They changed their money. ☐

4 a) He's watched a lot of TV. ☐
b) He watched a lot of TV. ☐

5 a) We've looked everywhere. ☐
b) We looked everywhere. ☐

6 a) You've read the book. ☐
b) You read the book. ☐

Pronunciation: stress in questions

7 **a)** Each of these questions has two main stresses (as in the example). Underline both stressed words.

Example: How <u>long</u> have you <u>lived</u> here?

1 How much did it cost?
2 How long was the film?
3 How old is your father?
4 How many did you buy?
5 How long has she worked there?

b) ◉◉ (27) Now listen and repeat.

A company report

8 a) Look at the top of John Taylor's company report.

Sonya Communications

Date of Report: 10th January 2002.

Name: John Taylor

Date of Birth: 4th January 1968.   **Place of Birth:** Portsmouth

Address: 10, New Road, Guildford (since 1980)

Married: (To Jane. 1994)

Children: Mark (5th April 1995) Maria (4th June 1997)

Current Position: Department Manager

Current Salary: £42,000

John Taylor began working for Sonya Communications in 1996.
He became Department Manager in 1998 and since then he

b) Write questions about John Taylor for these answers. (Remember – today is *10th January 2002*!)

Example:

How long has he lived in Guildford? ....   For 22 years.
How old is he? ......   34.

1 ....?

In Portsmouth.

2 ....?

For eight years.

3 ....? In 1994.

4 ....? Jane.

5 ....?

Two. A boy and a girl.

6 ....?

On 5th April 1995.

7 ....?

She'll be five this year.

8 ....? Since 1996.

9 ....? In 1996.

10 ....? £ 42,000.

A telephone conversation

9 a) Read this telephone conversation, and circle the correct forms.

A: Lamb Enterprises.

B: Hello. Can I (speak)/ **to speak** to John Lamb, please?

A: Who **calls** / **is calling**, please?

B: **It's** / **I am** Jane Starkey.

A: Can you **spell** / **to spell** that, please?

B: S – T – A – R – K – E – Y.

A: **Hold** / **Stay** the line, please.

A: I'm sorry – he's **on** / **in** a meeting, Ms Starkey.

B: Oh. Do you know when **will he** / **he'll** be back?

A: I'm afraid not. He **has been** / **is** in the meeting since 9:15.

B: Oh. OK. Can you **ask to him** / **ask him** to call me?

A: Certainly. **May** / **Do** I take your number?

B: Yes, sure. It's 456 7890.

A: Right. **I'll** / **I'm going to** tell him.

B: Thanks. Goodbye.

A: Goodbye.

b) 👓 (28) **Now listen and check.**

Pronunciation: sentence stress

10 **a)** Read these short telephone conversations. Underline the stressed word in each sentence B.

A	B
Example: Is that two three six, nine one four two?	No. This is two three <u>seven</u>, nine one four two.
1 Is that two three six, nine one four two?	No. This is two three six, nine one four three.
2 She's gone to Morocco.	Where has she gone?
3 Do you want to wait?	No I don't want to wait!
4 Is he at work?	No – he's at home.
5 He's in a meeting with Miss Love.	Who's he in a meeting with?
6 Can he phone you tomorrow?	No – I want to talk to him today.
7 The meeting finishes at 6:15.	When does the meeting finish?

b) 🔊 (29) Now listen and check.

Houses and rooms

11 Look at the pictures, and write the words in the crossword.

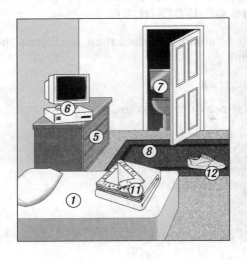
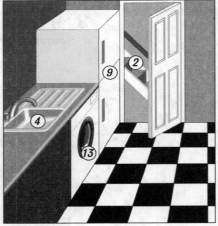
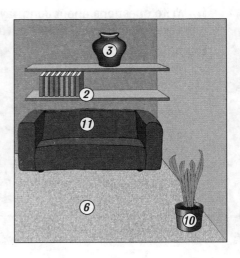

Across ▶

2 book ...

5 chest of ...

10 plant ...

13 washing ...

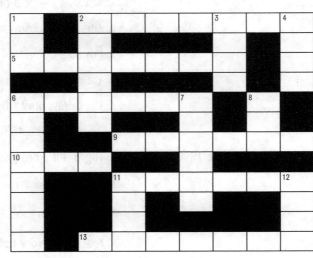

10 He loves me, he loves me not ...

Love story

1 Fill in the gaps in this story with the prepositions from the Word Box.

| off | out (x3) | in (x2) | up (x2) |

John and Jane met at a party and fell ....(1) love immediately. John was chatting ....(2) another girl when he first saw Jane. When he asked her ....(3), she said "Yes." The first time they went ....(4) together, he was late. They found they had a lot ....(5) common, and they were happy for some time.

But slowly they started to go ....(6) each other. They argued a lot, and once, Jane even threw John ....(7)!

Finally, after nearly a year, they split ....(8).

Pronunciation: /ɪd/

2 **a)** Look at these words. Tick (✓) the words where '-ed' is pronounced /ɪd/. Put a cross (✗) if it is not.

Examples: married ✓   divorced ✗

1 separated	☐	8 excited	☐
2 engaged	☐	9 decided	☐
3 fancied	☐	10 wanted	☐
4 chatted	☐	11 bored	☐
5 interested	☐	12 changed	☐
6 asked	☐	13 argued	☐
7 invited	☐	14 depressed	☐

b) 🔊 (30) Now listen and check.

Past Continuous

"What were you doing when I phoned you?"

3 **a)** This is Betty's "Come As You Are" party. Everybody has to come wearing exactly what they were wearing when Betty phoned them. Look at the picture and use a verb and a noun (if necessary) to make a sentence about each guest.

Joy   Vince   Sally

Bud   Mary   Trevor   Tony

Verbs			**Nouns**		
do✓	have	make	cake	house	garden
clean	work	fix	exercises✓	car	
sleep			shower		

Example: When Betty phoned ...
Bud *was doing* *exercises* .

1 Mary .... a ....

2 Joy .... a ....

3 Vince ....

4 Sally .... her ....

5 Trevor .... in the ....

6 Tony .... the ....

b) Now make questions about these people.

Example: *What was* Mary *doing* ?

1 .... Sally ....?

2 .... Trevor and Tony ....?

3 .... Vince ....?

Past Continuous and Past Simple

4 a) Match one background to one event.

Example: 1 = c)

Background	Event
1 it / not / rain	a) teacher / explain / exercise
2 Paul / paint / ceiling	b) I / steal / book
3 the students / not listen	c) we / start / picnic
4 Anne / look for / passport	d) police officer / stop / her
5 Carla / not drive / very fast	e) they / hear / news
6 they / listen / radio	f) he/ fall off / ladder
7 the shop assistant / not look	g) she / find / old diary

b) Now make sentences using the backgrounds (1–7) and events (a–g).

1 *It wasn't raining when we started our picnic.*

2 Paul .... when ....

3 The students .... when ....

4 Anne ....

5 Carla ....

6 They ....

7 The shop assistant ....

5 Fill in the gaps with *was(n't)*, *were(n't)* or *did(n't)*.

Example: *.Did.* she go to the party? I don't think she *.was.* there.

1 Sorry, we .... hear what you said. We .... listening.

2 **A:** .... you send that letter I gave you yesterday?

   B: Not yet – I .... just putting it in the envelope when you came in.

3 **A:** .... they studying French or German when they met?

   B: I don't know – I .... know them in those days.

4 He crashed because he .... concentrating. He .... talking on his mobile phone.

5 **A:** I .... ask for your advice! Go away!

   B: Sorry! I .... only trying to help!

6 **A:** Why .... at the evening class last night?

   B: I .... want to go because I .... feeling tired.

Pronunciation: sentence stress

6 a) Mark the two stressed words in each sentence or question before you listen.

Examples: <u>Where</u> was he <u>going</u>?
She was <u>writing</u> a <u>letter</u>.
He <u>wasn't</u> <u>listening</u>.

1 What was she doing?
2 They weren't working.
3 He was driving to Scotland.
4 What were you looking at?
5 I was trying to help.
6 She wasn't driving.
7 Why were they crying?
8 Who was she talking to?
9 You were reading a book.
10 How was she feeling?

b) 🔊 (31) Now listen and check.

Words with similar meanings

7 Match each word on the left (1–15) to a word on the right (a–o) which has the same or a similar meaning.

Example: 1 = f)

1 annoy	a) argue
2 row	b) sad
3 ring	c) pair
4 crazy	d) phone
5 couple	e) big
6 nice	f) irritate
7 small	g) mad
8 large	h) friendly
9 miserable	i) tidy
10 organised	j) little
11 calm	k) tasty
12 start	l) honest
13 delicious	m) quiet
14 truthful	n) handsome
15 good-looking	o) begin

Shades of anger

8 a) Complete the sentences (1–4) with words from the Word Box on the right.

1 She irritates ....

2 He gets on ....

3 It makes ....

4 She drives ....

| nerves | me (x3) | angry |
| crazy | my | |

b) This is Mr Moaner. He hates everything. Complete the sentences for the pictures (1–7) using the phrases in Exercise 8a), and the words from the Word Box below.

| my shower✓ | companies | kids | people on buses |
| my neighbours | people at the bus stop | | shop assistants |

1 It really _irritates_ me when ...._my shower_....... suddenly goes cold.

2 It .... on .... when .... have parties.

3 It drives .... when .... play music down the phone.

4 It .... me angry when .... ignore me.

5 It .... my nerves when .... don't queue.

6 It .... me when .... play football outside.

7 It .... my .... when .... use mobile phones.

Listening: Mr Moaner

c) 👀 (32) **Now listen to Mr Moaner.**

1 Which situation in the pictures (1–7) above is he talking about? ☐

2 Are these sentences true (T) or false (F)? Write T or F in the boxes.

a) People are there for three or four hours. ☐

b) Mr Moaner plays pop music. ☐

c) Mr Moaner says "How are you?" to them. ☐

d) He wants them to leave. ☐

e) He thinks things were better when he was young. ☐

f) He thinks the police are too young. ☐

Reading: *Living in Love*

Your TV letters

Dear *Your TV,*

I think *Living in Love* is the best programme on TV. I watch it every day – but why did they change the time? I used to watch it while I was having lunch from 1.30 until 2.00. Now it's on from 2:00 until 2:30, I don't know whether to have lunch before it, or to wait. Why must TV companies be so cruel?

Mrs Sally Absurd

Dear *Your TV,*

Somebody must do something about *Living in Love*. It was the best programme on TV. I say *it was* not *it is* because I haven't watched it since Sharneen died. How could the writers do that? Everybody loved Sharneen and wanted her to split up with her husband, Dan. His brother Sparky was perfect for her! Now what will happen to Dan? Will he inherit all her money and live forever with Kimmie? Sharneen was the nicest character – why didn't Dan die in that factory accident instead of her?

Mrs Dora Hamster

Dora,

Sarah Donavan who plays Sharneen wanted to leave to go to Hollywood when her contract ended. If you want to know what happens to Dan (and the writers say it will be something horrible) then you will have to start watching *Living in Love* again.

1:30 **The News.** National news and weather.
2:00 **Living in Love.** Episode 1278. Bongo plans revenge on Dan for his sister Sharneen's death. Kimmie decides to tell Dr Shane the truth as soon as he comes back from Tokyo. But Dan has other plans ...
2:30 **Gardening is Fun.** Building a Japanese garden.

Narleen Thomas who plays Kimmie in *Living in Love* says she really is living in love! "I've never been so happy," she said last week. "My new boyfriend, Craig Strong, is the love of my life." Craig and Narleen fell in love three weeks ago when they met at a film premiere. "I was in the middle of an interview when Craig came up and said 'Do you want to go to the cinema with me?' I just laughed!" Craig says "Narleen's the girl for me. She's really beautiful and rich. We're going to get married as soon as my wife agrees to a divorce." Craig has been married for two years to ex-Miss Australia Parloon Twerp, who is now a top fashion model.

---

9 a) Read *Your TV* (a) and the TV guide (b) and answer these questions.

1 Is *Living in Love* a weekly programme?

2 Did *Living in Love* used to be on at 2:00–2:30?

3 When did Dora stop watching *Living in Love*?

4 Did Dora want Sharneen to stay with Dan?

5 How did Sharneen die?

6 Will Dan live happily forever with Kimmie?

7 Is *Living in Love* on between two non-fiction programmes?

b) Read the newspaper extract (c) and fill in the gaps with the correct form of the verbs in brackets.

Example: Craig and Narleen (fall) .*fell*. in love three weeks ago.

1 Narleen (talk) .... to an interviewer when Craig (ask) .... her out.

2 Narleen (laugh) .... when Craig (ask) .... her out.

3 Craig (get) .... married two years ago.

c) Are these characters male or female? Write M (male) or F (female).

1 Bongo ☐   3 Dr Shane ☐

2 Kimmie ☐   4 Sparky ☐

Extend your reading Units 9–10

1 What is the highest price paid for a teddy bear? Read the article and find out.

Much more than toys

I recently asked my little girl who she loved most and she said, "Mum and Dad and ... my teddy." Apart from being one of the most treasured toys of both children and adults – forty per cent of all adults still have their childhood teddy bear – teddy bears can be worth thousands of pounds!

Americans have been collecting teddy bears since the 1930s. In Britain, however, interest in old teddy bears is quite recent, starting in the 1980s. Since then, prices have gone up dramatically: £2,090 for a blonde teddy bear in 1985; £5,720 for a yellow teddy only two years later; and £55,000 for Petsy Bear in 1989.

But the most famous bear in the collecting world is a cinnamon-coloured Steiff bear called Teddy Girl, made in 1904. A Japanese businessman paid an incredible £110,000 for it, in 1994. Part of the value came from the way the head was sewn down the middle, a feature that only seven Steiff bears have. However, the most important factor in determining the final price of Teddy Girl was the history and nostalgia that accompanied it.

Teddy Girl belonged to a well-known collector, British Army Colonel Bob Henderson, who took her with him everywhere, including the Normandy beaches on D-Day. There were also photographs, letters, paintings and a diary in which Teddy Girl appeared.

So, remember, if your bear has a metal button in its ear – the registered trademark of Steiff since 1905 – you could have a very valuable bear. If you have a coloured Steiff bear, it could be particularly valuable: Elliot, a bright blue teddy bear, sold for £49,500 in 1993!

2 Read the article again and choose the correct answers for 1–5.

1 Americans have collected teddy bears ...
a) for much longer than the British.
b) since the 1980s.
c) since prices went up.

2 What is the name of the most famous bear in the collecting world?
a) Petsy
b) Steiff
c) Teddy Girl

3 The bear is valuable because ...
a) it is very old.
b) it is made of a special material.
c) it has a history.

4 Teddy Girl was ...
a) a well-known collector.
b) in a painting.
c) a colonel.

5 What does it mean if your bear has a metal button in its ear?
a) It is very valuable.
b) It is a Steiff bear.
c) It was made in 1905.

3 **a)** Fill in the gaps in these sentences with prepositions. You can find the answers in the article.

1 Some old teddy bears are worth thousands ....
pounds. ☐

2 British interest .... old teddy bears is quite
recent. It started .... the 1990s. ☐

3 Elliot is the most famous bear .... the collecting
world. ☐

4 An American businessman paid £110,000 ....
Teddy Girl in 1994. ☐

5 The bear belonged .... a famous collector. ☐

b) Are the sentences in Exercise 3a) true (T) or false (F)? Write T or F in the boxes, then correct the false sentences.

11 If...

Second Conditional

1 a) What do the people in the pictures need? Add vowels to these words to make the names of the objects they need. Then match the objects (a–f) to the pictures (1–6).

a) c_lc_l_t_r

b) _mbr_ll_

c) m_ cr_w_v_

d) c*a*r

e) w_sh_ng m_ch_n_

f) d_ct__ _n_ry

1

She is at the bus stop. $\boxed{d}$

2

He doesn't understand the word. ☐

3

She doesn't know the answer. ☐

4

His clothes are dirty. ☐

5

He is wet. ☐

6

The meat isn't ready. ☐

b) Why do they need those things? Write a sentence for each picture.

1 *If she had a car, she wouldn't be at the bus stop.*

2 If he had a .... , he would understand the word.

3 If she .... a calculator , ...

4 If ....

5 ....

6 ....

2 Matt and Jackie have just moved into their new house. They've got nothing – not even money! Complete the dialogue.

MATT: *If we had a video, we could watch a film!*

JACKIE: Yes, I know. But we don't have a video, so we can't watch a film.

1 MATT: Well ... if we had .... , we .... listen to some music!

JACKIE: True, but we don't have a radio, so we can't listen to music.

2 MATT: If we , ... , we ....

JACKIE: Yes, but we don't have a lot of money, so we can't buy a video and a radio.

3 MATT: If ....

JACKIE: But we don't have a private jet, so we can't fly to New York.

4 MATT: OK. If ....

JACKIE: But unfortunately we don't live near the sea, so we can't go swimming.

5 MATT: You're so negative! You never agree with me!

JACKIE: Well, Matt, if you .... ideas, I .... with you!

3 **Tick the answers to these easy questions.
Then use the answers to make Second Conditional
sentences about imaginary situations.**

Examples: Are elephants very small?   Yes ☐ No ✓

               Can we ride them?   Yes ✓ No ☐

If elephants ......*were very small*........., we .....*couldn't ride them*......... .

Do people in the world disagree?   Yes ✓ No ☐

Is there world peace?   Yes ☐ No ✓

If people ....*didn't disagree*........, there ....*would be world peace*..... .

1 Do people have wings?   Yes ☐ No ☐

   Can they fly?   Yes ☐ No ☐

   If people ...., they ....

2 Does money grow on trees?   Yes ☐ No ☐

   Does it have any value?   Yes ☐ No ☐

   If money ...., it ....

3 Do we have bones?   Yes ☐ No ☐

   Can we stand up?   Yes ☐ No ☐

   If we ...., we ....

4 Can most birds fly?   Yes ☐ No ☐

   Do they have to walk everywhere?   Yes ☐ No ☐

   If most birds ...., they ....

5 Is every country exactly the same?   Yes ☐ No ☐

   Do people go abroad on holiday?   Yes ☐ No ☐

   If every country ...., people ....

6 Can animals talk to us?   Yes ☐ No ☐

   Do we eat meat?   Yes ☐ No ☐

   If animals ...., we ....

7 Does everyone speak the
same language?   Yes ☐ No ☐

   Do people have to study English?   Yes ☐ No ☐

   If everyone ...., people ....

Pronunciation: stress and weak forms

4 **a) Underline the stressed words
in these sentences.**

Examples: If he <u>spoke</u> <u>French</u>, he'd
<u>work</u> in <u>Paris</u>. If he <u>didn't</u> speak
<u>English</u>, he <u>wouldn't</u> have that <u>job</u>.

1 She'd work for Microsoft if she
could program computers.
2 If they didn't have to work, they'd
live on the beach.
3 I wouldn't work here if I could do
something else.
4 I could go anywhere if I had a lot
of money.
5 If I lived in America, I'd live in
New York.

b) **◉◉** (33) **Listen and check.
Notice how we pronounce
could(n't) /kədənt/ and
would(n't) /wədənt/. Listen again
and repeat.**

**c) Now try to say these
sentences.**

1 I could help you if you let me.
2 He'd come if you asked him.
3 If I could read his writing, I'd
understand the letter.
4 If she couldn't play the piano, she
wouldn't be happy.
5 People would be happier if they
could fly.

d) **◉◉** (34) **Listen and check.**

Giving advice

5 Sam has left his job, and is now unemployed. His friends have a lot of advice for him! Put his friends' advice in the correct box.

Have you thought about…? *borrowing some money*	you look through the papers
	you should go on holiday
	you go and live with your parents
Why don't …?	I would get a temporary job
	you ask your parents for money
	borrowing some money ✓
I think… .	you should move abroad
	looking for work in the USA
	I would ask for my job back
If I were you… .	doing some kind of training course
	I'd start my own business
	you should join the army

6 **a)** 🔊 (35) Listen to Lulu advising Sam. Tick (✓) the ideas in the list below which Sam thinks are good ideas.

1 take a year off ☐
2 take a part time job ☐
3 start his own business ☐
4 move to a different country
5 open a music shop ☐
6 rob a bank ☐
7 borrow money from the bank ☐
8 do some training ☐

b) 🔊 (35) Now listen to the conversation again, and fill in the gaps.

LULU: Oh, well, I don't know, really. I don't think you ……………… what you want. Maybe ……………… ……………… just ask for your job back.

SAM: Oh no. I ……………… ……………… that.

LULU: OK. Well, have you thought about ……………… your own business?

SAM: Hmm. That's a good idea. But what ……………… ……………… ……………… ?

LULU: Well, what are you ……………… ……………… ?

SAM: Music … drinking … Hey – I could open a pub.

LULU: No. I ……………… ……………… you should open a pub.

SAM: Well, what do you ……………… ……………… ……………… do?

LULU: Well. ……………… ……………… a music shop? I mean, selling CDs and videos …

SAM: Hey. Great idea. I've ……………… to work in a music shop ……………… I was a child. But it'll be really expensive!

LULU: Well, you ……………… rob a bank!

SAM: No, that's ……………… ……………… .

LULU: Well, borrow money from the bank, then.

SAM: Yes. I think ……………… ……………… . Maybe I will. Or maybe ……………… ……………… an astronaut …

LULU: Oh, Sam …

7 Rewrite these pieces of advice, starting with the words given.

Example: I think you should stop smoking.
Why don't ..*you stop smoking?*..

1 Have you thought about taking up a sport?

If I were you, ...

2 Why don't you learn Chinese?

Have you .... ?

3 If I were you, I'd get a divorce.

I think you ....

4 I think you should move house.

Have you .... ?

5 If I were you, I'd see a doctor.

Why don't ....

Find the mistake

8 Correct these sentences.

Example: If she were taller, she would look ~~as~~ *like* Naomi Campbell.

1 What would you do if you have a million pounds?

2 If I would be you, I would leave your job.

3 Have you thought in learning a language?

4 I would be very happy if she would be in love with me.

5 A: You should give up smoking.

B: This is a good idea.

6 If we were rich, we don't have to go to work.

7 If I didn't have my car, I wouldn't can go to work.

8 A: Why you don't phone her?

B: Oh no. I couldn't do that.

9 Has he thought about look for another job?

10 Where did you go if you could go anywhere in the world?

11 You shouldn't to complain so much.

12 If you were right, I don't would argue with you.

Jobs

9 In the Word Square, find the words which complete the sentences about jobs (1–10). Words can go down, across or diagonally ↓ → ↘ ↗.

T	M	U	S	I	C	I	A	N
R	M	R	K	B	O	A	X	D
A	L	I	O	P	Y	R	A	I
V	U	G	N	A	V	C	W	R
E	T	S	L	I	M	H	A	E
L	H	P	J	K	S	I	I	C
A	C	T	O	R	A	T	T	T
G	Y	E	O	P	G	E	E	O
E	L	V	K	M	E	C	R	R
N	Q	U	G	O	N	T	B	D
T	S	T	U	N	T	M	A	N

1 A _ _ _ _ _ _ _ _ _ _ _ organises holidays.

2 A _ _ _ _ _ _ _ _ plays the piano, the guitar, the violin ...

3 An _ _ _ _ _ _ _ _ _ designs buildings.

4 An _ _ _ _ _ works in films or in the theatre.

5 A _ _ _ _ _ _ _ _ makes films.

6 The Prime _ _ _ _ _ _ _ _ is the head of the government.

7 An _ _ _ _ _ _ finds work for actors or models.

8 A _ _ _ _ _ _ _ _ does the dangerous things in a film.

9 A _ _ _ _ _ _ works in a restaurant.

10 A _ _ _ _ wright writes for the theatre.

12 Love me, love my car

Listening: My ideal car

1 a) 🔲 **(36) Listen to four people talking about their ideal car. Complete the interviewer's question. Then match a car to each speaker.**

INTERVIEWER: What car .... if you ....

.... car in the world?

1 Janice ☐

2 Mandy ☐

3 Tim ☐

4 David ☐

b) 🔲 **(36) Listen again and tick (✓) the correct names.**

	Janice	Mandy	Tim	David
1 Which people want a comfortable car?				
2 Which person wants a reliable car?				
3 Which person *doesn't* mention safety?				
4 Which two people talk about speed?				
5 Which two people mention the price?				
6 Which person says the colour is important?				

Vocabulary: cars

2 Complete the words (1–10) from the picture.

1 p_s_e_g_r

2 d_i_e_

3 m_r_o_

4 w_n_s_r_e_ w_p_r

5 s_a_ b_l

6 s_e_r_n_ w_e_l

7 p_l_c_ o_f_c_r

8 r_a_ s_g_

9 d_i_g l_c_n_e

10 h_a_l_g_t_

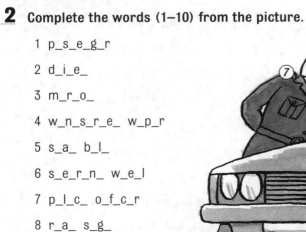

Describing people

Pronunciation: word stress

3 a) Read the three-syllable adjectives in the Word Box. Which have the stress on the first syllable (Ooo) and which have the stress on the middle syllable (oOo)? Fill in the table on the right.

> popular✓   creative✓   beautiful   relaxing
> different   ambitious   glamorous   unhappy
> efficient   terrible   romantic   untidy
> successful   unfaithful   wonderful
> welcoming   passionate   colourful   attractive

b) 👀 (37) Now listen and check.

Ooo	oOo
popular	creative

Star partner

4 Match one of the adjectives in the Word Box to each sign in the horoscope.

> reliable✓   pessimistic   lively   creative   traditional   jealous
> independent   proud   cautious   moody   passionate   tidy

Can the stars help you find your perfect partner?
Maybe they can!

Next time you're out with someone, just find their star sign – then look at our handy little list!

(♑) **Capricorn:** They're never late. If they say they'll do something, they do it. ....._reliable_.....

(♊) **Gemini:** They're always doing something. They're a lot of fun and full of life. ....

(♋) **Cancer:** They're happy one minute, miserable the next. Be careful! ....

(♓) **Pisces:** They're full of ideas and love making things. ....

(♌) **Leo:** Just like the lion in their sign, they look down on everyone. ....

(♍) **Virgo:** They're very organised. They like to know where everything is. ....

(♉) **Taurus:** They don't like change without a good reason. They like to do things in the old way.

....

(♎) **Libra:** They won't take any risks. They check everything before they move. ....

(♈) **Aries:** They're very possessive. They love you, but they don't trust you! ....

(♏) **Scorpio:** They're like fire! They love, and hate and get angry with real emotion! ....

(♒) **Aquarius:** They always look on the dark side. ....

(♐) **Sagittarius:** They like to work alone. They don't need people. ....

Direct and Reported Commands

5 a) **What are they saying? Use a verb and a noun from the Word Boxes to fill in the gaps.**

Verbs	Nouns
get out✓ open cross smoke✓ repeat make	bag car✓ road question coffee pipe✓

1

"_Get out_. of the ......_car_......!"

2

"Please, don't ...._smoke_.... your ....._pipe_..... in here."

3

"Sorry. Can you .... the ...., please, Sir?"

4

"................. your ....!"

5

"Can you .... some ...., darling?"

6

"Don't .... the .... here."

b) **Now report the commands in Exercise 5a) using _tell_ or _ask_, and make any necessary changes.**

1 The policeman ..._told_... him _to get out of his car_ .

2 The woman _asked_ him _not to smoke his pipe_ .

3 The boy .... the teacher ....

4 The customs officer .... him ....

5 She .... her husband ....

6 She .... her son ....

Pronunciation: sentence stress

6 a) **Underline the stressed words in these sentences and questions.**

Examples: She <u>told</u> me to <u>hurry</u>.
Did they <u>ask</u> him <u>not</u> to <u>speak</u>?

1 She told me to leave.
2 Did he tell her not to go?
3 They asked him to stay.
4 They told me to stop it.
5 Did he ask you to read it?

b) 👓 (38) **Listen and check.**

Ask or tell?

7 **Make sentences with _ask_ and _tell_ using the pronouns in brackets.**

Example: "Don't do it." (she, him)
She told him not to do it.

1 "Please, don't tell anyone." (she, them)

She asked ....

2 "Slow down!" (he, her)

....

3 "Don't drive so fast!" (he, her)

....

4 "Could you sign this form, please?" (she, them)

....

5 "Get out of here!" (they, her)

....

6 "Marry me – please!" (he, her)

....

7 "Please, don't turn the TV on." (she, him)

....

8 "Shut up!" (he, him)

....

Do you remember? Units 9–12

Present Perfect: *for* or *since*?

1 Fill in the gaps using the Present Perfect form of the verb in brackets. Then put *for* or *since* in the boxes to complete the sentences.

Example: A: How long ...*have*... you ...*had*... that beautiful watch? (have)

B: This? ☐ *Since* ☐ my wedding anniversary.

1 A: How long .... she .... there? (live)

B: ☐ ☐ last summer, I think.

2 I .... only .... her ☐ ☐ three weeks. (know)

3 I .... a holiday ☐ ☐ 1996. (not/have)

4 A: .... you .... Jane recently? (see)

B: No. No-one .... her ☐ ☐ ages. (see)

5 A: Tom .... terribly depressed ☐ ☐ he lost his job. (be)

B: I know. He .... to anyone ☐ ☐ weeks! (not / speak)

Past Simple or Past Continuous?

2 Fill in the gaps with the Past Simple or the Past Continuous of the verbs in brackets.

Last Monday I (leave) ....[1] the office early, because I (want) ....[2] to buy a ticket for a concert at the Royal Festival Hall. When I (walk) ....[3] along Charing Cross Road I (meet) ....[4] Peter, an old friend of mine. He (go) ....[5] to the Royal Festival Hall too, so we (decide) ....[6] to walk together. When we (arrive) ....[7] at the theatre, there was only one ticket left. While Peter and I (argue) ....[8] about who should have the ticket, an old woman (come) ....[9] and (buy) ....[10] it!

Giving advice

3 Look at the conversations (1–4). Complete what A says, using the verbs in brackets. Then choose a verb from the Word Box (in the correct form) to complete the advice that B gives.

> rob ✓   study   ask   give up   go

Example: A: If I *were* (be) rich, I *would buy* (buy) a yacht!

B: Why *don't* you *rob* a bank?

1 A: If she .... (love) me, I .... (be) so happy.

B: Why .... you .... her out?

2 A: If I .... (know) what was wrong, I .... (feel) more relaxed.

B: I think you .... to a doctor.

3 A: I .... (get) a better job if I .... (have) better qualifications.

B: If I were you, I .... at an evening school.

4 A: If I .... (not smoke), I .... (not/have) this terrible cough.

B: Have you thought about ....?

On the telephone

4 a) Fill in the gaps in these short telephone calls.

1 A: Hello?

B: Hello. ......*This*...... is Dan Holmes. Is .... Springfield Records?

A: No, I'm .... not. You've got the .... number.

B: Oh – I'm very ....

A: ....'s OK. Goodbye.

2 A: Hello. Springfield Records.

B: Hi. .... is Dan Holmes.

A: .... do you .... that, please?

B: H–O–L–M–E–S. .... I speak to Terry, please?

A: Certainly. .... the line, please.

b) 🔊 (39) Now listen and check.

Extend your reading Units 11–12

1 Read the article and answer these questions.

1 How did Ricky become interested in cars? ....

2 What kind of music does he like? ....

3 What does Ricky do with his cars? ....

The Classic Car Collector

Ricky Van Shelton* has always had a deep love for old cars. As a young boy, a friend of his, Jack Clay, would let Ricky drive his 1960 Corvette. He was too small to reach the clutch and the steering wheel was almost bigger than he could handle. But the thrill and excitement of driving such a powerful vehicle was unforgettable!

When Ricky was fourteen years old, his brother Ronnie tried to persuade him to sing with his band. But Ricky was into Rock 'n' Roll and Ronnie was into Country ... Ricky just wasn't interested. But then Ronnie made Ricky an offer he couldn't refuse: "If you sing with us, I'll let you drive my 1964 Fairlane." It was more than the teenage boy could resist ... a beautiful 2-door, 4-speed, 289 engine. He loved the car and quickly fell in love with Country music.

Ricky purchased his first classic car in 1973; he paid $150 for a 1941 Hudson. He started his collection

with these simple rules: he never paid more than $500 for a vehicle, worked on it constantly and traded it for a better car. In those days, he could afford only one vehicle at a time.

Since his success in the music business, Ricky has fulfilled one of his lifelong dreams. "I've always wanted to have my own junkyard, so when I bought my 150-acre farm near Nashville I started collecting some old cars that needed fixing up. I'll never forget the day my business manager, Chuck Flood, visited the new property. I was driving him around through the fields when he asked me when I was going to throw the junk cars away. I replied, 'Throw them away? I've just had them brought here!' I'll never forget the look on Chuck's face!"

During the past seven years, Ricky has restored several classic cars, including some from the fifties, sixties and seventies. His collection includes Fords, Chevrolets and a Cadillac. It totals almost fifty vehicles ...

Ricky Van Shelton is a well-known Country music singer in the USA.

2 Complete the table with these expressions from the text.

clutch   steering wheel   junkyard   Fairlane   Chevrolet   fixing up   4-speed engine   property   to drive around   worked on   Ford   Cadillac   fields   restored

car parts	actions	places	make of car
clutch	fixing up	junkyard	Fairlane

3 Are these statements true (T) or false (F)? Write T or F in the boxes.

1 In 1960 Ricky wasn't allowed to drive because he was too young and too little. ☐
2 The "*beautiful 2-door, 4-speed, 289 engine*" in paragraph 2 is a car. ☐
3 When he was fourteen Ricky liked cars better than Rock 'n' Roll music. ☐
4 A lot of Ricky's cars needed repairs when he bought them. ☐
5 Ricky wanted to have a lot of room to park his old cars. ☐

4 Ricky says "*I'll never forget the look on Chuck's face*" Why? What was Chuck thinking? (paragraph 4)

Extend your grammar Units 9–12

1 Fill in the gaps with words from the Word Box. You don't need all the words.

> intelligent for going have haven't interested
> down me much might mustn't driving read
> reading so to was were will would

Chinese horoscopes

I saw an advert for a Chinese astrologer while I was ....(1) the newspaper the other day. It told you to call a number to learn about your personality. I ....(2) never believed in horoscopes, but this was different: a Chinese astrologer! I picked up the phone and dialled the number. A voice asked me ....(3) use the numbers on the phone to dial my year of birth. A few moments later another voice told ....(4) I was a rat. A rat? The recording continued: "According to Chinese astrology, rats are charming and sociable. They are also reserved and ....(5). They make good business people and politicians. They are very active, ...(6) they tend to make and spend a lot of money." Actually, I have been a teacher ....(7) twenty-five years and I have never made ....(8) money. I suppose the other characteristics ....(9) be true. The recording continued with plans for my future: "You need a change in your life. You are ....(10) to get married soon." Now I was shocked! If I wanted a change in my life, I ....(11) go on a holiday. I am not married and I am definitely not going to get married soon. This recording was really ....(12) me crazy and the call ....(13) costing me a lot of money. So I put ....(14) the phone and I ....(15) told anyone about it ... well, until now!

2 Complete the second sentence so that it means the same as the first sentence.

Example: When did you move to Dublin?
How *long have you lived.* in Dublin?

1 I got this watch for my twentieth birthday; I'm twenty-five now.
I have .... five years.

2 If I had a computer, I could finish this report at home.
I don't .... I can't finish this report at home.

3 When I'm at home, my mum makes me get up early.
When I'm at home, I ....

4 Why don't you throw away that old chair?
If I were .... that old chair.

5 "Fill in this form, please." said the receptionist.
The receptionist asked .... form.

3 Read the conversation between Lisa and Madame Stella, a fortune-teller. Circle the correct forms.

MME STELLA: I can see it very clearly now in the cards. You are **having / going to have** very good luck in the next few months. I think you **should / can** buy a lottery ticket or go to the casino.

LISA: Good! What about love?

MME STELLA: Oh, dear. I can see that you **will fall / are falling** in love with a tall handsome man ...

LISA: That can't be right. I **go / am going** out with someone. We **are / have been** together for five years.

MME STELLA: You will **break up / have broken up** with your boyfriend and **meet / met** this new man.

LISA: Oh! I just wanted to know if we would get married this year ...

Extend your writing Units 9–12

An informal letter

1 **What's Shona's problem? Read her letter and find out.**

> 9, Ruston Rd
> Glasgow
> G20 8HQ
>
> 23rd May 2000
>
> Dear Kim,
>
> Thank you for your last letter. It was good to hear from you after so long. How are you? How's your family? What's it like living on a farm away from civilization? You haven't really told me much about your new life.
>
> In your letter, you ask me about my love life. Well, … I've got some news, but I don't know if it's good or bad. I've met the perfect man and I think I'm in love. The problem is that he's from New Zealand. He's working in Glasgow for a few weeks and then he'll go back home. I met him two weeks ago and we have become much more than good friends. Now I don't know what to do.
>
> If I really fall in love with him, I'll be so unhappy when he leaves, but if I don't tell him how I feel, I might not have the opportunity again. What should I do? Help me, please. You know me and I know that you're very good at helping with decisions.
>
> Please, write soon. I haven't got much time. I would call you if you had a phone!
>
> Love,
>
> Shona

2 **Look at the structure of the letter and answer these questions.**

1 Did Shona write her name at the top of the letter?
2 Did she include her address?
3 Did she write Kim's name and address at the top of the letter?
4 Where did Shona put the date?
5 How did she start the letter?
6 Did she put a comma (,) or a colon (:) after Kim's name?
7 How did she finish the letter?

Writing Tip

If you don't want to say *Love* at the end of your letter, you can say *Best wishes*.

3 **Write Kim's answer to Shona's letter. Use the following prompts to help you.**

your address

the date

Dear Shona,

Introduction *(use Shona's letter for ideas).*

You ask … new life. We … happy here. It's true … but life is simple … air is clean!

Why … always do … same thing? Can't … find … normal man? I think you should / shouldn't … tell him. If I were you, I'd / I wouldn't worry … future … If he loves … too … why don't you ask … stay?

Write back soon … tell … all about it.

Love,

13 What a holiday!

Countable and uncountable nouns

1 Fill in the gaps with *is* or *are*.

1 Today's news .... very good.

2 Your hair .... getting very long.

3 The people .... shouting at the police ...

4 ... but the police .... not reacting.

5 Everyone .... feeling a bit nervous.

6 How old .... this furniture?

7 Your advice .... very good.

8 The information you gave me .... very interesting.

9 The children .... playing football outside.

10 Hey! Where .... my luggage?

11 No-one .... at work at the moment.

12 The problem .... that he never listens to a word I say.

13 .... the workmen here yet?

14 Someone .... always on duty at reception.

15 Oh no! My money .... in my wallet, in my other jacket.

Pronunciation: vowel sounds

2 **a)** Circle the word in each list which has a different vowel sound.

Example: r**oa**d br**o**ken c**oa**ch (b**oar**d) c**oa**st

1 sp**or**t w**or**d w**or**ld p**er**son s**ur**fing

2 **ae**robics c**are**ful st**air**s **are** **air**port

3 w**a**ve br**ea**k sp**ea**k str**aigh**t compl**ai**nt

4 w**a**ter th**ough**t **aw**ful t**augh**t sh**ow**

5 c**ou**ple gr**ou**p h**u**rry c**u**stomer p**u**blic

6 s**i**gn bl**i**nds s**igh**ts r**i**ng pr**i**vate

7 cr**ui**se b**ui**ld s**ui**t fr**ui**t j**ui**ce

b) 🎧 (40) Now listen and check.

Present Perfect + *yet*

Questions

3 **a)** Giles and Gillian are on holiday at the *Club Torso* holiday resort. Write Giles' questions to Gillian, using the words in brackets.

Examples:

(go / surfing) *Have you been surfing yet?*

(play / baseball) *Have you played baseball yet?*

1 (do / painting class) .... ?

2 (go / horse-riding) .... ?

3 (do / aerobics class) .... ?

4 (play / tennis) .... ?

5 (go / jet skiing) .... ?

Negative sentences

b) Now look at Gillian's diary, and complete her answers to the questions in Exercise 3a). It is now *Thursday afternoon*.

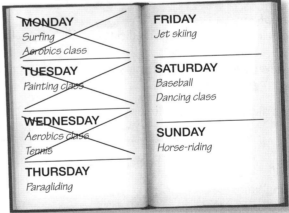

Examples: *Yes, I have. I went surfing on Monday.*
No. Not yet.

1 Yes, I .... I .... a painting class on

....

2 No. ....

3 Yes, ... Monday and

....

4 ....

5 ....

How much / How many / How long ... ?

4 Complete these questions with *How much, How many* or *How long*.

Example: *How much...* money do you have in the bank?

1 .... were you in France?

2 .... times have you been to Mexico?

3 .... time did you spend in Germany?

4 .... was the flight? Less than three hours?

5 .... days' holiday do you have this year?

6 .... do they pay you in that company?

7 .... have you worked for them?

8 .... people work in your company?

9 .... time do you spend with your family?

10 .... does it take you to get to work?

Predictions: *be going to do*

5 Choose a verb or phrase from the Word Box, and make predictions using *going to*.

> get better✓   not win the race✓   rain   die
> not get the job   get a divorce   not pass the exam

Examples:

She has reacted well to the medicine and she's very strong.
She's going to get better.

He never exercises and he smokes and drinks too much.
He isn't going to win the race.

1 The sky is full of grey clouds.

....

2 He's 103 years old and he has been very sick for a long time.

....

3 He hasn't got the right qualifications and he didn't make a good impression at the interview.

....

4 She has finally discovered that he is having an affair. She's really angry.

....

5 He doesn't study, he never listens in class and he never does the homework.

....

Prepositions: movement and location

6 a) Put these prepositions into the correct place in the table.

> in✓   onto✓   off   on   out of   into

(A) location	(B) movement	movement – opposite to (B)
in	....	....
....	*onto*	....

b) Now fill in the gaps in the sentences with prepositions from Exercise 6a).

1 The police officers are all .... the building.

2 Joe is .... the roof.

3 Jack is getting .... the window.

4 John is jumping .... the roof.

5 Jim is getting .... the car.

6 Jerry is jumping .... the car.

Present Perfect / Present Continuous / *going to*

7 **a)** Make three sentences for each picture (a–f), using the groups of words.
(They are not in the correct order.)

a)

- run
- rob / bank
- fire / gun

1 *He has robbed a bank.*

2 *He is running.*

3 *He is going to fire his gun.*

b)

- put on / hat
- leave / house
- put on / coat

1 He has .... his coat.

2 He is .... on ....

3 He is going to ....

c)

- eat / big meal
- pay / bill
- smoke cigars

1 They ....

2 They ....

3 They ....

d)

TAXI?

- go / airport
- phone/ taxi
- pack / cases

1 ....

2 ....

3 ....

e)

- drink too much
- crash
- drive too fast

1 ....

2 ....

3 ....

f)

- put on / make-up
- have / shower
- get dressed

1 ....

2 ....

3 ....

b) Now rewrite the *going to* sentences in Exercise 7a), using *have not ... yet*.

Picture a: *He hasn't fired his gun yet* .

Picture b: He .... the house ....

Picture c: They .... the bill ....

Picture d: ....

Picture e: ....

Picture f: ....

Listening: complaints

8 a)  (41) **Listen to the two conversations and answer these questions. Complete the table.**

Who are the two people?
Where are they?
What are they talking about?

Who?	Where?	What about?
1 customer and ...		
2		buying a ...

b) **Before you listen to a customer complaining to the mechanic at his local garage, read the sentences below. Who do you think will say each sentence? Write C (customer) or M (mechanic).**

1 Just give me my car back. C
2 What can I do for you? ☐
3 Let me speak to the manager. ☐
4 Is it ready yet? ☐
5 I'm a professional. ☐
6 It could be two weeks, it could be a month. ☐

c) ☐☐ (42) **Listen and check. Then listen again. Are these sentences true (T) or false (F) ? Write T or F in the boxes.**

1 The mechanic told him to come on Tuesday. ☐
2 The customer's car is German. ☐
3 There was a problem with the passenger door. ☐
4 The mechanic has to get the parts from Germany. ☐
5 The mechanic has taken the wheels off the car. ☐
6 The mechanic knows how much it will cost. ☐
7 The customer speaks to the manager. ☐

Holidays and hotels

9 **Read the clues and fill in the crossword.**

Across ▶

1 The lift doesn't work. You'll have to use the ...
4 "Good morning. Can I ... you?"
6 "This is Room 409. There's no whisky in the ..."
9 Tomorrow I'm going to ... a 2-person aeroplane!
11 GIINDV: put in the right order for a water sport.
13 There are 120 ... staying in this hotel.
15 You take this with you when you travel.
17 You need snow to do this.
19 "The air ... in our room doesn't work."
21 "The repairman will see ... it as soon as possible."

Down ▼

1 A water sport: wind- _ _ _ _ _ _ _.
2 "I'll send someone to fix it straight ... ."
3 "Could you put ... shampoo in Room 208?"
5 GAPILINRAGD: put in the right order for a sport.
7 "The people in the next room are very ... . We can't sleep!"
8 "The ... on the main window in Room 909 is broken. We can't pull it up."
10 A water sport: _ _ _ skiing.
12 "Excuse ... . I have a problem."
14 They all took a coach trip to see the ... of the city.
15 "This is Room 501. The ... on the bathroom door doesn't work."
16 Enid isn't here. She's ... horse-riding with Rebecca.
17 You take it on holiday: _ _ _ _ case.
18 "This is Room 604. There isn't any ... water in the shower."
20 "This is Room 605. There's ... soap in the bathroom."

14 Crime doesn't pay!

Crime

1 Complete the sentences with words from the Word Box. You can use the same word more than once.

> houses   money   people   jewellery
> televisions   flats   banks   wallets   silver

1 A burglar: a) steals ....

b) robs ....

2 A pickpocket: a) steals ....

b) robs ....

3 A bank robber: a) steals ....

b) robs ....

Listening: describing people

2 a) Put the words and phrases in the Word Box into the appropriate category in the table.

> tall✓   a small nose✓   blue trousers✓
> in his / her thirties   fit   jeans   middle-aged
> make-up   a round face   a suit   dark skin
> some jewellery   short hair   glasses
> long fingers   a dress   grey eyes   about 26
> thin   quite short   small hands

She/He's got ...	She/He's ...	She/He's wearing ...
...a small nose...	...........tall..........	..blue trousers...
....	....	....
....	....	....
....	....	....
....	....	....
....	....	....
....	....	....

b) (43) Listen to a policewoman questioning a witness. Which person is the witness describing?

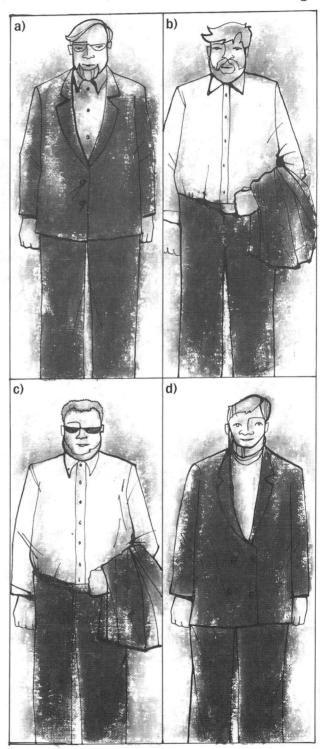

a)   b)

c)   d)

The passive: Present Perfect and Past Simple

3 **a)** Look at the picture of a busy police station. What has happened to the people? Fill in the speech balloons using a verb from the Word Box.

steal✓   mug   rob   steal   burgle   steal

a) My car _has been stolen_ !

b) I ....

c) My house .... again!

f) My wallet ....

e) All our computers ....

d) The bank .... !

b) Now complete the police officer's questions to the people in the picture, using the Past Simple Passive or the Present Perfect Passive.

a) When _was your car stolen?_

Has your car ever _been stolen_ before?

b) Where .... ?

.... you ever .... before?

c) When .... your house .... ?

How many times .... ?

d) When .... the bank .... ?

e) But . . . How .... ??!!

f) When .... ?

c) A week later, all the people phone the police station to see if any progress has been made. Complete the police officer's answers.

 "Have you found my car ?"

"I'm sorry, your car _has not been found yet_ ."

 "Has anybody seen the mugger?"

"I'm sorry, sir. The mugger .... yet."

 "Have you caught the burglar?"

"I'm sorry, madam. .... "

 "Have you questioned any witnesses?"

"Yes! Three witnesses .... "

 "Have you found the computers?"

"Yes. All the computers .... "

 "Have you arrested the thief?"

"I'm sorry, sir. .... "

Passive or active?

4 Change these sentences into the Passive or the Active.

Examples: Somebody broke that window yesterday.
That window was broken yesterday.
A book has been written about that crime.
Someone has written a book about that crime.

1 People rob banks every day.

Banks ....

2 My bicycle was stolen last night.

Someone ....

3 People have broken every law.

Every ....

4 The murderer was never found by the police.

....

5 They made that law 200 years ago.

....

6 People are arrested by the police every day.

....

7 They watched the house all night.

....

8 The killer has been seen!

....

Pronunciation: sentence stress

5 **a)** Underline the stressed word in these sentences.

1 He was mugged.
2 They were robbed.
3 Was he killed?
4 Were they hurt?

Underline the *two* stressed words in these sentences.

1 When was this done?
2 Has this been checked?
3 Who was killed?
4 Yes, they were.

Underline the *three* stressed words in these sentences.

1 John was arrested on Saturday.
2 How can it be finished so quickly?
3 Sandy was attacked and robbed.

b) 🔊 (44) **Now listen and check.**

Passive or active?

Present Perfect

6 Fill in the gaps with *has* or *has been*.

1 That boy .... broken another window.

2 Jane .... invited to Sarah's party.

3 Did you know that John .... released from prison?

4 The hospital .... treated 200 patients.

5 This clock .... broken for twenty years.

6 Ivan .... asked to attend the conference, but he doesn't want to go.

7 My heart .... examined by experts.

8 No-one .... worked there since last summer.

9 Steve .... lost his watch again.

10 A woman's bag .... found in the ladies' toilets.

Reading: Agatha Christie

Part One

7 **a)** Fill in the gaps in Part One with *in, at, to* or *by*.

Agatha Christie

You don't have to be interested ....(1) crime to know who Agatha Christie is. She is one of the most popular novelists ever, and her books have been translated into more languages than those of any other writer.

Agatha Christie's childhood was a comfortable one. She was born ....(2) the south-west of England (probably ....(3) 1891 – nobody knows for sure) to parents who were quite rich. Her mother did not think that girls needed to go ....(4) school, so she stayed ....(5) home, where she was taught ....(6) her parents and people who worked ....(7) the house.

b) Now answer these questions about Part One.

1 How do we know that Agatha Christie is one of the most popular novelists ever?

2 Where did she study?

Part Two

c) The regular Past Simple verbs are underlined in Part Two. In which of these verbs is *...ed* pronounced /ɪd/ (as in *hated*)?

During the First World War, Agatha <u>worked</u> in a hospital, where she <u>learned</u> all the information about poisons which she <u>used</u> in her books later. In 1914 she <u>married</u> Archibald Christie. It seems they were happy for a long time, but in 1926 Archie told her that he <u>loved</u> another woman and he <u>wanted</u> to leave her. Soon after that, Agatha <u>disappeared</u>. Her empty car was found. Was she dead? Did she kill herself? Or did someone murder her? Police <u>asked</u> thousands of people to help them find her.

d) ⦿⦿ (45) Listen and check.

e) Now answer these questions about the story so far.

1 About how old was Agatha when she married Archibald Christie?

2 How long were they together?

3 In Part One, *"Her books have been translated."* means *"People have translated her books."*

Now change these sentences in the same way.

She was taught by her parents.

Her parents ....

Her empty car was found.

Somebody .... car.

People were asked to help the police.

The police ....

Part Three

f) Fill in the gaps with the words from the Word Box.

> finally ✓   met   after that   until
> successful   during   memory

.....*Finally*..... the police found her in a hotel in the north of England – she seemed to have lost her ....(1), but the truth about the mystery has never been discovered. ....(2), she travelled alone to the Middle East, where she ....(3) Max Mallowan, who she married a year or two later. ....(4) the Second World War she worked in a hospital. After the war she continued to be happy and ....(5), writing plays and novels ....(6) her death in Wallingford, Oxfordshire in 1976.

g) Now write questions about Agatha Christie for these answers.

1 Where .... found?

In a hotel in the north of England.

2 .... in the Middle East?

Max Mallowan.

3 .... him?

One or two years later.

4 ....?

During the Second World War.

5 ....?

About 85.

Extend your reading Units 13–14

1 What is Expedition Titanic? Read this advertisement to find out.

Expedition Titanic

Who hasn't heard of the Titanic? Since it sank in 1912, people have returned to the subject again and again in books and films.

We now proudly announce Expedition Titanic, a once-in-a-lifetime opportunity to join a scientific expedition to the wreck of the Titanic. A limited number of adventurers will travel in a submersible to the resting place of the Titanic, 3,775 metres under the sea ...

Highlights:
Participants in the expedition will live aboard a scientific research ship. They will attend lectures and instruction sessions given by a number of experts. Participants will dive to the site of the wreck aboard a submersible. This experience will be recorded on videotape, to keep as a souvenir of the expedition.

Important Notice:
We strongly believe that the wreck of the Titanic and the surrounding remains should be respected both as a historic site and as a cemetery. The wreck will be seen from the outside and nothing will be taken, except photographs and videos, and nothing taken away, except memories.

Health Notice:
Passengers have to certify that they do not have any medical or psychological condition or physical disability that could be a risk to themselves or other passengers. We reserve the right to disqualify any participant at any time during the programme if the person's health puts at risk the safe operation of the expedition.

For more information call Expedition Titanic.
Phone 1 212 373 7624

2 Read the advert again and answer these questions.

1 What happened in 1912?

....

2 Will there be a lot of participants on this expedition?

....

3 What will the expedition take from the wreck?

....

4 What can happen if you are ill during the expedition?

....

3 Find the words (1–5) in the advertisement and match them with their meanings (a–e).

1 once-in-a-lifetime   a) a physical problem
2 wreck   b) a ship which has sunk, or
3 dive   is badly damaged
4 memories   c) things you remember
5 disability   d) to go underwater
               e) very special, unique

4 Match the beginnings of sentences (1–5) with their endings (a–f) to make complete sentences.

1 Have you heard   a) aboard our ship.

2 I never read   b) about disasters.

3 You'll live   c) as a souvenir.

4 The dive will be recorded   d) in the expedition.

5 You can take the videotape home   e) of the Titanic?

6 Several companies are involved   f) on videotape.

7 Lectures will be given   g) people's safety at risk.

8 The company can't put   h) by experts.

15 What are you talking about?

One(s) and *the one(s)*

1 Fill in the gaps in the conversations with *one(s)* or *the one(s)*.

Examples:

A: What video shall we get?

B: *One* that doesn't have Tom Hanks in it.

A: Which of those men is your uncle?

B: *The one* wearing the red hat.

1 A: What sort of bike you are going to buy?

B: .... that isn't very expensive.

2 A: Do you want that cake?

B: Yes. Give me .... with the chocolate on top.

3 A: Which shoes are you talking about?

B: .... I wore at Julia's wedding.

4 A: Has he got a car?

B: No – I don't think he's got ....

5 A: What kind of books do you usually read?

B: .... with happy endings!

Defining relative clauses

Who or *which*?

2 Fill in the gaps with *who* or *which*.

Example: Is this the man *who* spoke to you?

1 I want a car .... goes very fast.

2 We only employ people .... can work hard.

3 It's a natural medicine .... really works.

4 I'd like a sofa .... is the same colour as the chairs.

5 You'll meet someone .... will fall in love with you.

6 This is a pen .... is also a lighter!

7 Is this the man .... stole your car?

8 She's the only person .... really listens to me.

9 The doctor .... examined you isn't here today.

10 It's one of those toys .... needs batteries.

The one(s)

3 Change the answers to the questions (1–5) to include *the one* or *the ones*.

Example: "Which shoes?" "I wore them at Kathy's party."

"The ones which I wore at Kathy's party."

1 "What book?" "I lent it to you last week."

....

2 "What exams?" "We'll do them next July."

....

3 "Which disk?" "It has all the accounts information on it."

....

4 "Which politician?" "He introduced the new tax."

....

5 "What CDs?" "You bought them yesterday."

....

Definitions: *who, which* or *that*

4 Look at the definitions, and then fill in the crossword.

1 Things that you cut paper with.
2 A person who has seen a crime.
3 People who come to parties.
4 A person who kills another person.
5 A person who steals.
6 A thing that you draw with.
7 A woman who acts in films or plays.

1	S	C	I	S	S	O	R	S
2								
3								
4								
5								
6								
7								

Now write a definition of the word in the grey boxes.

....

5 a) Match the people (1–6) to the names below (left).

Ian Fleming	1	a)	compose *The Eroica Symphony*
Picasso	☐	b)	write the "James Bond" books
Billie Holiday	☐	c)	fly solo to Australia in 1930
Marie Curie	☐	d)	sing *Strange Fruit*
Beethoven	☐	e)	discover radium
Amy Johnson	☐	f)	paint *Guernica*

b) Now match each person (1–6) to a phrase in the list (a–f) and make a sentence.

① ②

③ ④

⑤ ⑥

1 *Ian Fleming was the man who wrote the "James Bond" books.*

2 ....

3 ....

4 ....

5 ....

6 ....

Pronunciation: strong and weak forms

6 a) We can pronounce *that* in two ways. Stressed /ðæt/ or unstressed /ðət/. Read these sentences and tick the correct pronunciation.

Examples:	/ðæt/	/ðət/
I didn't know that!	✓	☐
I didn't know that you were French.	☐	✓
1 The man that stole the money escaped.	☐	☐
2 Who said that?	☐	☐
3 That doesn't matter.	☐	☐
4 This one or that one?	☐	☐
5 This is the school that I went to.	☐	☐
6 I went to that school.	☐	☐
7 Don't do that!	☐	☐
8 I'm sure that he knows.	☐	☐
9 I hate that sort of film.	☐	☐
10 Are these the glasses that you lost?	☐	☐

b) 🔊 (46) Now listen and check.

Look, look like or *have got*?

7 Write sentences about the pictures (1–3), using words from the Word Box, and *look*, *look like* and *have got*.

angry ✓	dangerous	twins
short black hair	blonde hair	Hillary Clinton
sad	Robert de Niro	long black hair

1 2 3

1 She looks ...*angry*...

   She looks like ....

   She's got ....

2 He looks ....

   He looks like ....

   He's got ....

3 They ....

   ....

   ....

Countable and uncountable nouns

8 a) Look at the pictures. Write T (thing) S (stuff) or Ts (things) next to each one.

b) Fill in the gaps with *is a thing*, *are things* or *is stuff*, then match the sentences.

Example: 1 = i)

1 A key ....*is a thing*...........   a) you use to dry yourself.

2 Shampoo ....*is stuff*........   b) you use to cook with.

3 Paperclips ....   c) which takes your temperature.

4 A thermometer ....   d) you wear to see better.

5 Vitamin pills ....   e) you take to feel healthier.

6 Fly spray ....   f) which keep papers together.

7 A towel ....   g) you wash your hair with.

8 Toothpaste ....   h) you use to clean your teeth.

9 Glasses ....   i) you use to open a door.

10 Olive oil ....   j) which kills flies.

c) Now write your own definitions using *a thing*, *things* or *stuff*.

1 A diary ....   3 A mobile phone ....

2 Suntan lotion ....   4 Gloves ....

Listening: School reunion

9 a) (47) **Look at the picture. Steven and Jane meet at their school reunion. Listen once and match the first names to the surnames.**

Jane   Moore
Steven   Morris
Gary   Dobson
Elizabeth   Pike
Michael   Farley
Louise   Carter

b) (47) **Are these sentences true (T) or false (F)? Listen again and write T or F in the boxes.**

1 Jane arrived before Steven. ☐
2 Gary used to be very popular. ☐
3 Gary has got long black hair. ☐
4 Elizabeth is very fat. ☐
5 Michael went out with Louise Morris. ☐
6 Jane thinks Michael was rude. ☐
7 Steven liked Michael. ☐

c) (47) **Listen again and tick (✓) the one(s) who was / were good at sports.**

Gary ☐   Michael ☐   Steven ☐

d) (47) **Listen again, and fill in the gaps in this part of the conversation.**

JANE: Right! Steven! Of course. How are you?

STEVEN: Fine. .... did you .... ?

JANE: A few .... ago. ....
.... have you been here?

STEVEN: Oh. About an hour. It's incredible. Everyone
.... so different. We all ....
.... our parents.

JANE: I know. I can't recognise ....

Asking questions

10 **Look at the answers below. Then complete the questions.**

Example: ..*Where*.. does he ..*come from*..?
He comes from Chicago.

1 .... does he .... ?
He's tall and blonde.

2 .... does he .... ?
In a flat near the city.

3 .... does he .... ?
He's a doctor.

4 .... does he .... ?
At 6:30 every morning.

5 .... does he .... ?
Usually suits and ties.

6 .... does he .... ?
French and English and a bit of German.

7 .... does he .... ?
About $100,000 a year.

8 .... does he .... ?
Two. A boy and a girl.

9 .... is he .... ?
He's friendly, kind and generous.

10 .... does *generous* .... ?
It means he likes giving things to people.

16 The strangest thing happened to me ...

Say or tell?

1 Fill in the gaps with the correct form of *say* or *tell*.

1 I'll .... you what I really want.

2 What were you .... when I interrupted?

3 I've .... him three or four times!

4 "Hello," she .... "How are you?"

5 Would you .... that again, please?

6 They didn't .... me anything about it.

7 I .... you, but you didn't listen.

8 Don't .... anything to anyone.

9 I asked her, but she .... "No."

10 .... me that story about the princess.

Reported Speech

2 Many words change when we report speech – not only the verbs. Match
the spoken words (1–10) to the reported words (a–j).

Example: 1 = e)

Spoken	Reported
1 "today"	a) there
2 "tomorrow"	b) the day before
3 "yesterday"	c) the next day
4 "here"	d) his / her
5 "my"	e) that day

Spoken	Reported
6 "now"	f) the following week / year
7 "last week / year"	g) that / the
8 "next week / year"	h) before (that)
9 "this"	i) then
10 "ago"	j) the week / year before

3 Complete this table, changing from Direct speech to Reported speech
(beginning "*She said ...*") or vice versa. Make any other necessary changes.

Direct Speech	Reported Speech
"I want to go today."	*She said she wanted to go that day.*
"My brother is teaching in Greece."	She said her brother was teaching in Greece.
1 "He doesn't work in this company."	She said
2	She said he wrote to her every week.
3	She said Mark still lived in France.
4 "We are leaving tomorrow."	They
5 "Our house is the one next to the shop."	They
6	She said she loved that kind of book.
7 "My sister doesn't want to come."	He
8	She said Julian didn't know the answer.
9 "I often go there on Saturdays."	She
10	She said she wasn't ready.

Listening: A visitor from space

4 **a)** (48) Jimmy Chatter is interviewing a visitor from space on his TV chat show. Listen and fill in the gaps.

JIMMY: So, Bloop, my friend. **Where** .... [1] **you** .... [2] **from?**

BLOOP: I .... [3] **from Planet Ditko.**

JIMMY: That's lovely. And **how long** .... [4] **the journey take?**

BLOOP: It .... [5] **four earth-minutes.**

JIMMY: That's incredible! .... [6] **you** .... [7] **in a flying saucer?**

BLOOP: We travel by a method you .... [8] understand.

JIMMY: Super. And **where** .... [9] **you** .... [10]**?**

BLOOP: We .... [11] .... [12] with your Prime Minister.

JIMMY: Great. A lovely person. And **how long** .... [13] **you staying on earth?**

BLOOP: We .... [14] .... [15] until your planet is destroyed!

JIMMY: Oh dear!

b) Change the questions and answers **in bold** in the interview to Reported Speech, using *ask* or *tell*.

Example: Jimmy *asked Bloop where he came from.*
        Bloop *told Jimmy that he came from Planet Ditko.*

Jimmy ....

Bloop ....

Jimmy ....

Bloop ....

Jimmy ....

Bloop ....

Jimmy ....

Bloop ....

Jimmy ....

Bloop ....

So, such or *such a(n)*

5 Fill in the gaps in these sentences with *so, such* or *such a(n)*.

1 I had no idea he was .... clever.

2 He was fired because he was .... bad teacher.

3 Another new car? She must be .... rich!

4 They have .... stupid fights about nothing.

5 She is .... artistic.

6 She does .... interesting paintings.

7 The whole situation was .... embarrassing. I didn't know what to do.

8 I have never seen .... bad film. It was terrible!

9 He is .... untidy – he never cleans anything.

10 I've had .... awful day. Everything went wrong!

Pronunciation

6 **a)** Read these words, and tick the correct pronunciation for each word.

	/eɪ/ (day)	/iː/ (see)	/aɪ/ (try)
1 money		✓	
2 mind			
3 child			
4 delay			
5 believe			
6 played			
7 crime			
8 complain			
9 receipt			
10 increase			

b) (49) Listen and check your answers.

Do you remember? Units 13–16

1 **a)** Mr Fixit works at the River Rose Hotel. He is checking his diary for this week. It is now *Wednesday night*. Look at what he has and hasn't done. Then answer the questions (1–5).

MONDAY

Morning: Fix the taps in 107. ✓
Afternoon: Clean the windows. ✓

TUESDAY

Morning: Repair the washbasin in 805. ✓
Afternoon: Clean the carpets. ✓

WEDNESDAY

Morning: Buy paint for reception area. ✓
Afternoon: Paint the reception area. ✓

THURSDAY

Morning: Take the car to the garage.
Afternoon: Cut the grass.

FRIDAY

Morning: Clean the swimming pool.
Afternoon: Change the curtains in 307.

SATURDAY

Morning: Collect the car.
Afternoon: Fix the wardrobe in 208.

SUNDAY

Day off!

Examples:
Has he fixed the taps in Room 107?
Yes, he has. He fixed them on Monday.
Has he cleaned the swimming pool?
No, not yet. He's going to clean it on Friday morning.

1 Has he cleaned the windows?

....

2 Has he repaired the washbasin in Room 805?

....

3 Has he fixed the wardrobe in Room 208?

....

4 Has he collected the car?

....

5 Has he had a day off this week?

....

b) Now write the questions for these answers.

Example: *Has he cleaned the carpets?*
Yes, he has. He cleaned them on Tuesday morning.

1 ....?

No, not yet. He's going to change them on Friday afternoon.

2 ....?

Yes, he has. He bought it this morning.

3 ....?

No, not yet. He's going to take it tomorrow morning.

4 ....?

Yes, he has. He painted it this afternoon.

5 ....?

No, not yet. He's going to cut it tomorrow afternoon.

Test your English!

1 a) Tick (✓) the correct sentences.

Example: *(d)* Were you speak English?
           (w) Have you speak English?
       ✓ *(h)* Do you speak English?

1 *(o)* She is cleverer that her sister.
  (r) She is cleverer as her sister.
  (a) She is cleverer than her sister.

2 *(s)* What is she look like?
  (v) What is she like?
  (d) How does she look like?

3 *(e)* What does this word mean?
  (a) What does this word means?
  (y) What means this word?

4 *(t)* That's the man who live next door.
  (r) That's the man who he lives next door.
  (y) That's the man that lives next door.

5 *(o)* He hasn't got much money.
  (i) He hasn't got no money.
  (e) He hasn't got many money.

6 *(e)* I take a shower when he telephoned.
  (u) I was having a shower when he telephoned.
  (y) I was take a shower when he telephoned.

7 *(d)* I was so surprised.
  (w) I was such surprised.
  (n) I was such a surprise.

8 *(i)* *Othello* was written for Shakespeare.
  (n) *Othello* was wrote in 1560.
  (o) *Othello* was written in 1560.

9 *(k)* You have been to New York last summer.
  (n) You have been to New York three times.
  (l) You have been to New York didn't you?

10 *(a)* Can I give you some advices?
   (l) Can I give you an advice?
   (e) Can I give you some advice?

11 *(o)* Came fifty people to the party.
   (h) Fifty people they came to the party.
   (a) Fifty people came to the party.

12 *(l)* She wasn't listening to me.
   (y) She hasn't listening to me.
   (i) She couldn't listening to me.

13 *(p)* If I would be rich, I'd buy a new car.
   (l) If I had £10,000 I'd buy a new car.
   (d) If I win the lottery, I'd buy a new car.

14 *(t)* If I see him, I'll tell him.
   (i) If I'll see him, I'll tell him.
   (s) If he come, I'll tell him.

15 *(g)* Do you have some informations about this?
   (l) Do you have any informations about this?
   (h) Do you have any information about this?

16 *(e)* He told me he was leaving the next day.
   (b) He said me he was leaving the next day.
   (t) He told he was leaving the next day.

17 *(f)* Isobel will have four next month.
   (g) Isobel will be four years next month.
   (e) Isobel will be four next month.

18 *(x)* It was such a big house.
   (z) It was a so big house.
   (y) The house was such big.

19 *(u)* He asked me to don't speak so fast.
   (a) He asked me not speak so fast.
   (e) He asked me not to speak so fast.

20 *(p)* She didn't make her homework.
   (m) She didn't her homework.
   (r) She didn't do her homework.

21 *(d)* We live in this house for three years.
   (e) We have lived in this house since three years.
   (c) We have lived in this house for three years.

22 *(e)* When do you going to finish?
   (i) When are you going to finish?
   (y) When will you going to finish?

23 *(s)* There aren't any people in there.
   (r) There aren't some people in there.
   (d) There isn't any people in there.

24 *(i)* The film wasn't so interested.
   (n) The film wasn't any interesting.
   (e) The film wasn't really interesting.

25 *(d)* I worked in France while the war.
   (h) I worked in France when the war.
   (s) I worked in France during the war.

b) The letters you have ticked make a question.
Write them down here, then look through your
book to answer the question.

$\underline{H}$ _ _ _   _ _ _   _ _ _ _   _ _ _   _ _ _

_ _ _ _ _ _ _ _ ?

If your answer to the question is "No", then you
know what to do!

Extend your reading Units 15–16

1 Heather Woods was found dead in her flat on 27th March. Her ex-boyfriend, Kevin Sharpe is the main suspect. Read the report of the police investigation. Has Kevin got an alibi? (An *alibi* is someone or something which proves the suspect was somewhere else when a crime was committed.)

CRIME REPORT INTO THE DEATH OF HEATHER WOODS

Background information

- Ms Woods lived alone with her dog, in a quiet neighbourhood.

- Ms Woods didn't go to work on 26th or 27th March, so her colleague and friend, Amy Carr, went to Ms Wood's flat on 27th March.

- Ms Carr found the victim's dead body. She had been killed with a large kitchen knife. The front door hadn't been forced open, so police believe Ms Woods knew her murderer.

- At the autopsy, the police doctor said that victim had died on the evening of 25th March.

- Ms Carr was the last person to see the victim alive, on the 25th March, when they left the office at the end of the day. Ms Carr said that her friend was worried because she had received several annoying phone calls from her ex-boyfriend, Kevin Sharpe.

Notes on the main suspect, Kevin Sharpe

- The suspect said that he had left work at 5.45 p.m. and had driven straight home (a 15-minute drive). He said that he had spent the evening at home, on his own, and had only gone out to walk the dog.

- He ordered a pizza from Magic Pizza at about 6 p.m. It was delivered 30 minutes later. The pizza delivery man said that he couldn't remember Mr Sharpe. Magic Pizza's records say that a pizza was delivered to Mr Sharpe's address, but there is no signature to prove this.

- The suspect said that he had walked his dog at around 8 p.m. and Mr Land, a neighbour, told the police that he had seen someone with a big dog outside Mr Sharpe's flat at about this time. He assumed that this person was Mr Sharpe.

- The suspect said that he had gone to sleep after the TV film *A Murder Suspect* or *Suspect of Crime*, he couldn't remember exactly. The police have checked and Channel 4 showed the film *A Murder Suspect* from 8.30 to 10.15 that evening.

- The police have questioned another of the suspect's neighbours, Mrs Lattice, and she said that she could hear the sound of Mr Sharpe's TV on the evening of 25th March.

- The police searched the suspect's flat and found two interesting items: a card from a dog sitter service, which will look after your dog for you (including taking it for walks); and an empty bottle of dog sleeping tablets.

- **The police are confident that they know who murdered Heather Woods.**

2 Finally Kevin confessed to the murder. Read the report again and answer these questions.

1 Who do you think walked Kevin's dog? Kevin or the dog sitter?
2 Who do you think ordered the pizza? Kevin or the dog sitter?
3 Who do you think watched the film? Kevin or the dog sitter?
4 How did Kevin keep Heather's dog quiet?
5 How did Kevin kill Heather?

If you need still need help to find out how Kevin did it, look at the box at the bottom of page 79.

3 These sentences about the crime are in Reported Speech. Look carefully at the way the verb changes in the example, then rewrite the sentences in Direct Speech.

Example: The doctor **said** that the victim **had died** on 25th March.
DOCTOR: "The victim **died** on 25th March."

1 The suspect said that he had walked his dog at around 8 p.m.

MR SHARPE: ....

2 The suspect said that he had gone to sleep after the TV film.

MR SHARPE: ....

3 Mr Land told the police that he had seen someone with a big dog.

MR LAND: ....

Extend your grammar Units 13–16

1 Fill in each gap in the text with one word from the Word Box. There are some words you won't need.

> so talking asked at badly because by during explained home in interesting jealous later next questioned until up was

Getting into trouble

Matt decided to go out after he and Maggie had a row ....(1) dinner.

Matt just wanted to have a quiet drink at the pub. A young woman ....(2) the bar started a conversation with him and he didn't notice she was ....(3) to him because she wanted to make her boyfriend ....(4). What happened .... (5) wasn't hard to predict: Matt .... (6) hit in the face by the boyfriend. He wasn't ....(7) hurt, but he didn't realise what was happening ....(8) he saw blood coming out of his nose. Then he stood ....(9) and hit the person in front of him. Unfortunately, it was a policeman and Matt was arrested immediately and taken to the police station. He was examined ....(10) a doctor and then ....(11). Matt ....(12) what happened and apologised to the policeman. He was allowed to go home, ...(13) he made a phone call. Thirty minutes ....(14) Maggie came to the police station and drove him home without a single word. "A night in jail would be better than this," Matt thought on the way .... (15)

2 Complete the second sentence so that it means the same as the first sentence.

Example: You can take great pictures with this new camera.
This is a camera you *can take great pictures* with.

1 Mitchie Friend is a thief. He has recently stolen a Picasso from an art gallery.

Mitchie Friend is the .... a Picasso from an art gallery.

2 Someone broke into my house last night.

My house .... last night.

3 Betty gave me a dictionary for my birthday. Would you like to see it?

Would you like to see .... gave me for my birthday?

4 I never knew he was so interesting.

I never knew he was .... person.

5 How many times did they wash this jumper?

How many times was ....

6 My sister only weighs 47 kilos, so she cannot give blood.

My sister cannot give blood .... 47 kilos.

7 "I just love California," said the actress.

The actress said that ....

8 She said that she was leaving the next day.

" .... ", she said.

Extend your writing Units 13–16

A formal letter

1 Read this letter and find out why Mr Carver is complaining.

12, Harrington St.
Liverpool
L70 1BS
UK

Expedition Titanic
1212 Baxter Ave N
New York, 98109
USA

10th June 2000

Dear Sir / Madam

I have just returned from Expedition Titanic and I was very disappointed with the whole trip. The organisation was terrible and the experience was very different from what was described in your advertisement.

First, the ship was late and we had to wait at the departure point for two hours in the rain. Then, when we finally got to the site of the wreck, one of the submersibles broke down. I had to wait for another five hours to go underwater. Finally, when it was my turn to get inside the submersible, at nine o'clock in the evening, it was so dark that I fell into the cold sea. As a result, I was ill for two weeks.

I think it is your responsibility as organisers of an expedition to guarantee that your equipment works and your passengers are safe. Consequently, I demand a full refund of the money I paid. If I don't receive a satisfactory reply within a few weeks, I will have to take legal action.

I look forward to hearing from you.

Yours faithfully

George Carver

George Carver

2 Look at the letter and answer these questions:

1 Did Mr Carver write his name at the top of the letter?
2 Did he include his address?
3 Did he write the name and address of the company he was writing to?
4 Where did he put the date?
5 How did he start the letter?
6 How did he finish the letter?

Writing Tip

If you don't know the name of the person, you start your letter with *Dear Sir/Madam* and finish *Yours faithfully*. If you know the name of the person, you begin with *Dear Mr / Mrs / Ms Johnson*, and finish with *Yours sincerely*.

3 You want to complain about a trip you have taken. Use Mr Carver's letter as a model to write your letter. Take notes under these headings:

1 *Introduction:*
Why are you writing the letter?
Where did you go?
What was wrong?

2 *Your trip:*
What happened exactly?
How did it affect your holiday?
Did anyone try to help?

3 *Your demands:*
Why do you think you are right?
What type of compensation do you want?
What will you do if they don't give you compensation?

Answer Key with Tapescripts

Answer Key

Unit 1 Finding out about people

1a)

1 Who 2 Where 3 What 4 What
5 Where 6 What 7 What 8 What 9 When
10 Where

b)

b) = 3, 5   c) = 7, 8   d) = 6, 9   e) = 2, 10

c)

1 What does your wife do?
She's a doctor, too.
2 Do you both work in the same hospital?
No, we don't. She works in a private clinic.
3 Does she like her job?
I don't know. I think she's happy. Why don't you ask her?
4 And do you have any children?
Yes. Two. Caroline's sixteen and Ian's ten.

2a), b) and c) 〔oo〕 (1)

BETTY:

I'm a doctor in a private clinic in Central London. I work long hours most days – even at the weekends sometimes. I'm not working today, but I have to be available in case there's an emergency. They can always contact me. But I enjoy my job – I find it very interesting.

CAROLINE:

My favourite subject at school is politics. I know it sounds boring, but I think it's really important. I want to work in Latin America when I leave school – I'm studying Spanish at the moment on a part-time course. Our teacher speaks so beautifully – his name's Pablo – he's got such a lovely voice.

IAN:

I go to school every day and I do homework every evening. It's stupid. At the moment I'm writing to all the famous Hollywood stars because I want to go there and be rich and famous. Because school is stupid and all the other kids are stupid. Especially Trevor.

a) and b)

1 Betty 2 Caroline 3 Betty 4 Caroline
5 Ian

c)

1 She works long hours (at a private clinic).
2 She isn't working.
3 She wants to work in Latin America.
4 He wants to go to Hollywood and be rich and famous.
5 She's studying Spanish.

6 He does homework.
7 He's writing to Hollywood stars.

3

1 meet 2 choose 3 's happening
4 don't talk 5 're discussing 6 comes
7 lives 8 's working 9 works
10 's looking 11 'm working 12 eat

4

2 = d) Do you often go out?
No, I don't go out very often.
3 = e) Do you clean your teeth twice a day?
Yes – in the morning and before bed.
4 = f) How often do you do exercise?
I hardly ever do exercise.
5 = a) How do you usually go to work?
I often take the bus.
6 = b) When do you practise your English?
I practise all the time.

5a)

1 Could you carry my tray for me?
2 Can you get me a coffee?
3 Would you mind putting this cushion under my foot?
4 Could you stop the bus, please?

b)

1 Would you like me to close the window?
2 Shall I order a taxi?
3 Would you like me to get your coat?
4 Shall I help you with your homework?
5 Would you like me to come and see you on Sunday?

c)

1 A: Would you like me to get you a sandwich?
B: Thanks a lot.
2 A: Shall I copy these letters?
B: No, I'll do it.
3 A: I'll make some photocopies.
B: Thanks. That's really nice of you.
4 A: Would you like me to get you a coffee?
B: Don't worry. I'll get one later.

6a), b), c) and d) 〔oo〕 (2)

1 current affairs
2 newspaper headlines
3 intensive course
4 professional musician
5 interior design
6 computer skills

7a) 〔oo〕 (3)

Example: cheap
1 ship
2 it
3 beat
4 cheek
5 list

7b) 〔oo〕 (4)

Example: feet
1 fit
2 fit
3 feet
4 feet
5 feet

8a)

1 appointment 2 machine 3 office
4 meeting 5 boss 6 computer 7 post
8 temp 9 diary 10 e-mail 11 urgent

b)

Does anybody know how to fix the photocopier?

2 Money matters

1a), b), c) 〔oo〕 (5) and d) 〔oo〕 (6)

(1) ...ght	(2)...ew
caught	threw
brought	knew
taught	flew
bought	grew
thought	blew

2a) and b) 〔oo〕 (7)

Examples: saved wasted✓
1 finished
2 wanted✓
3 changed
4 decided✓
5 listened
6 disappeared
7 started✓
8 died
9 looked
10 watched

3a) and b) 〔oo〕 (8)

Little Johnny came home from school one day, and his Dad asked him, "So, how did your history exam go?" .... Silence ... then "Not very well," Johnny said. "It was too difficult! All the questions were about things that happened before I was born!"

a)

a), b), c), a), b), c)

4

Across	Down
1 spent	2 paid
3 died	4 earn
6 wins	5 saved
8 afford	7 shop
10 owe	9 statement
14 tipped	11 wealthy
16 on	12 invest
17 as	13 wasted
18 sold	15 is
19 lent	18 still

21 eat   20 need
23 see   22 broke
24 inherited   25 no
26 to
27 generous

5
1 I didn't use to go to work.
2 I used to copy what all my friends did.
3 I didn't use to feel confident with other people.
4 I used to be frightened of everything.
5 I used to believe in Father Christmas.
6 I didn't use to worry about money.
7 I used to hate Monday mornings.
8 People didn't use to ask for my opinion.
9 Time didn't use to pass so quickly.
10 My older brother used to hate me.

6a) and b)
1 used to walk   2 (no change)
3 (no change)   4 used to meet
5 used to tell   6 didn't use to answer
7 used to speak   8 used to take
9 (no change)   10 (no change)
11 (no change)   12 used to wake
13 (no change)   14 (no change)
15 (no change)   16 (no change)

7b)
1 *Boot Up* is shorter than *Adam*.
2 *Adam* is more expensive than *Boot Up*.
3 *Boot Up* is more successful than *Adam*.
4 *Boot Up* is cheaper than *Adam*.
5 *Adam* is more interesting than *Boot Up*.
6 The members of Rubbish are younger than the members of Fishmonger.
7 The magazine thinks *Adam* is better than *Boot Up*.
8 The magazine thinks *Boot Up* is worse than *Adam*.

8a) b) and c) 〇〇 (9)
ANDREW: How about *Casablanca*? I know we've seen it before, but I love this film.
BECKY: Oh no, I don't think so. I mean it's so boring. I want something colourful.
A: Mmm. OK – well how about a good old Marilyn Monroe film. Great technicolor romantic comedies. And she's so beautiful.
B: Do you think so? I don't. I think she's ridiculous! She's fat and really ...
A: I'm sorry, Becky, I don't agree. She's fantastic-looking. And the films are funny.
B: Really? I think they're for children, and anyway, we've seen all these films before. Let's see a new film. How about *Romance Again*? It came out last year and people said it was ...

A: Oh, you're joking! Kevin Teflon is a terrible director! I hate him! He's so sentimental! Watching his films is like eating too much chocolate!
B: I like chocolate.
A: So do I. So do I. I love it. But I *don't* like *too much* chocolate. That's all I'm saying.
B: I don't want to argue, Andrew.
A: Neither do I, Becky. Can we just get a video without three hours of discussion?
B: I suppose so ...
A: How about *Night Kiss*?
B: Hey! Yeah! Good idea!
A: What?! Do you agree?!
B: Absolutely!
A: Incredible.

a)
1 likes *Casablanca*
2 likes Marilyn Monroe
3 dislikes the director of *Romance Again*
4 likes chocolate
5 likes *Night Kiss*

b)
1 D   2 D   3 D   4 A   5 A

Extend your reading Units 1–2
1 1 = T   2 = F   3 = T   4 = T   5 = F (they don't get a salary)   6 = T
2 1 = T   2 = T   3 = F (they often take part in excursions)   4 = T   5 = T
3 1 = c)   2 = a)   3 = e)   4 = f)   5 = d)   6 = b)   7 = g)

3 It's your life!
1a)
1 = b)   2 = c)   3 = a)   4 = d)
b)
Text a): 1 left   2 told   3 couldn't   4 had   5 wanted   6 started   7 gave
Text b): 1 ran   2 didn't get   3 missed   4 found   5 spoke   6 needed
Text c): 1 exploded   2 got   3 wanted   4 met   5 lived   6 moved   7 inherited   8 died
Text d): 1 got   2 looked   3 spoke   4 phoned   5 saw   6 joined   7 went   8 hated
c)
1 He had an important business meeting.
2 San Francisco.
3 Three days.
4 Eighteen.
5 Twenty.
6 Five years.
2 〇〇 (10)
I was very bored, being married to Brian. He used to go out every night at nine o'clock, and sometimes he didn't come back until nine the next morning. I didn't

have anyone to talk to. He told me he was at political meetings, but sometimes I could smell perfume in his hair. I think he used to meet another woman at those meetings. But ... It doesn't matter. Life's better without him!

3a) and b) 〇〇 (11)
Example: He told_us to stop_it.
1 He missed_a meeting.
2 I liked_her father.
3 She wanted_everything.
4 My parents bought_a small house.
5 Does_it make_any difference?
6 She said they lived_in_Africa.
7 She studied_economics_at_university.
8 I_needed_all the money.
9 Sometimes_I think_about_him.
10 Listen_and_understand.

4a)
1 went   2 fell   3 broke   4 cut   5 cried
6 locked   7 drank   8 argued   9 found
10 ate
b)
1 Joanna remembers going to Italy with her mum and dad.
2 Charlotte remembers falling off a bicycle when she was five or six.
3 Philip remembers breaking his brother's favourite toy car.
4 Mark remembers cutting his head very badly in a football game.
5 Victor remembers crying because he lost his mum in a supermarket.
6 Julia remembers locking herself in a wardrobe by accident.
7 Valerie remembers drinking paint when she was three.
8 Graham remembers arguing with all his teachers at school.
9 Simon remembers finding some very old coins in a field.
10 Noel remembers eating all his sister's birthday cake.
c)
1 What did Philip break?
2 Why did Victor cry?
3 When did Charlotte fall off a bicycle?
4 Who did Graham argue with?
5 Where did Simon find some very old coins?

5a) and b) 〇〇 (12)

	/tuː/	/tə/
1 I remember going to Italy.	✓	
2 We went to France.		✓
3 He wanted to make some money.		✓
4 She wanted to earn some money.	✓	
5 He was kind to everyone.	✓	
6 She was never kind to me.		✓

7 They'd like to do something different. ☐ ✓

8 We didn't want to eat bread and water. ✓ ☐

6

1 brought up 2 looked after 3 fell off
4 look for 5 listen to 6 waited for
7 go out 8 get up 9 talked about
10 run away

7b)

1 Where was Bruce Lee born?
2 When was he born?
3 What was his father's name?
4 Why was he sent back to the USA?
5 Where did he work (while he was studying)?
6 What was his first big film called?
7 When did he die?
8 How many people attended his funeral?

c)

1 martial arts 2 decade 3 returned
4 demonstrating 5 tournament
6 assistant 7 enormous 8 attended
9 following

4 Hooray for Hollywood!

1

1 exciting / bored 2 interesting
3 surprised 4 amusing / boring 5 excited
6 confusing / moving 7 depressing
8 tired

2a) and b) 🆗 (13)

1 exercises✓
2 languages✓
3 bottles
4 courses✓
5 experiences✓
6 tenses✓
7 headlines
8 times
9 sentences✓
10 chocolates

3

Down	Across
1 Brad	1 blockbuster
2 Cage	6 Caprio
3 star	7 director
4 Rain	10 do
5 action	11 science fiction
6 comedy	12 Hollywood
8 Can	16 thriller
9 Niro	19 part
10 done	20 Spielberg
11 stunt	
12 horror	
13 Were	
14 chase	
15 young	

17 lots
18 Yul

4a)

2 Both Mel and Joe have driven a fast car.
3 Only Mel has used a machine gun.
4 Only Mel has visited Africa.
5 Only Mel has fought a wild animal.
6 Only Mel has climbed a mountain.
7 Both Mel and Joe have broken a bone.

b)

1 He hasn't used a machine gun.
2 He hasn't visited Africa.
3 He hasn't fought a wild animal.
4 He hasn't climbed a mountain.

c)

2 "I climbed Mount Everest in 1991."
3 "I drove a Ferrari six months ago."
4 "I visited Mozambique in 1998."
5 "I fought a lion when I was in Mozambique."
6 "I broke my leg two years ago."
7 "I used an Uzi machine gun in *Police Brutality*, in 1996."

d)

1 Has / hasn't 2 did
3 Was / wasn't / was 4 Has / has 5 Have
6 were 7 didn't 8 did 9 was
10 Were /weren't

5a)

adjective	superlative
rich	richest
beautiful	most beautiful
tall	tallest
expensive	most expensive
funny	funniest
successful	most successful
handsome	most handsome
dangerous	most dangerous
good	best
bad	worst

b) and c) 🆗 (14)

OK! Now are you listening? I want people to love the stars – OK? I want the guy to be a real hero! He has to be big! Get me the tallest actor in Hollywood! At least two metres tall!
And they both have to look fantastic! I want the most handsome actor and the most beautiful actress you can find!
Who won the Oscar for the best actor last year? ... Get him! ... I don't care how much he costs! I don't care if this is the most expensive film in history! Money isn't important! ...
No, I don't want Tommy Tomson! He's no hero! He's never taken a risk. Taking a bus is the most dangerous thing he's ever done! Find a real man! ...

And I want people to laugh! Who is the funniest writer in Hollywood at the moment? ... OK! Get them all! And the director! ... Who? ... No, I don't want him! He's terrible! *Night Kiss* was the worst film I've seen in my life! Awful!
Now what is the most successful film of the last ten years? What's made the most money? ... Get me the director of that film! OK, OK, we'll need lots of money! So we'll get lots of money! ... Who is the richest man in Hollywood? ... Me? Oh ... excellent!

b)

1 most handsome 2 most beautiful
3 best 4 most expensive
5 most dangerous 6 funniest 7 worst
8 most successful 9 richest

6a)

1 = d) 2 = f) 3 = a) 4 = e) 5 = g) 6 = c)
7 = b)

b)

1 awful 2 miserable / broke
3 beautiful 4 fabulous / love

Do you remember? Units 1–4

1

Bob:

Bob didn't use to smoke.
Bob used to go to the library.
Bob didn't use to copy from other students.
Bob used to arrive early.
Bob used to listen to the teacher.

Ted:

Ted used to listen to his Walkman in class.
Ted used to smoke.
Ted didn't use to do homework.
Ted used to have fights.
Ted didn't use to study for exams.

2

1 started 2 Have you seen 3 did you buy
4 Have you tried 5 have never been

3a) and b) 🆗 (15)

JOHN: Where are you going? It's half past one in the morning!
JANE: I'm not going anywhere. I'm opening the door because it's hot in here!
JOHN: So why are you wearing a coat? You don't usually wear a coat in bed!
JANE: Er ...erm ... I'm going to the kitchen for a glass of milk. I have a glass of milk at half past one every morning.
JOHN: I don't believe you! I think you're lying!
JANE: OK. It's true! I'm leaving you! I'm running away!
JOHN: Fine. But please be a bit quieter. I'm trying to sleep!
JANE: Sorry. Bye.

Extend your reading Units 3–4

1a)

1= F   2 = T   3 = F

2

1 costumes   2 audience   3 audition
4 lines   5 movie

3a)

1d)   2c)   3a)   4b)

b)

1 had the opportunity to   2 played a part
3 keep in shape   4 become stars

Extend your grammar Units 1–4

1

1 for   2 better   3 went   4 later   5 them
6 into   7 full   8 Every   9 while   10 how
11 so   12 it   13 one   14 to   15 because

2

1 you like me to   2 as old
3 I didn't use to smoke
4 the most intelligent   5 putting the key
6 my job boring   7 you mind
8 is better at mathematics

Extend your writing Units 1–4

1

There are two possibilities: 2, 1, 4, 3;
or: 2, 4, 1, 3.

2

a) = 2   b) = 1   c) = 4   d) = 3

5 Playing by the rules

1a)

1 No fishing.
2 Wet road. Please drive carefully.
3 No eating or drinking in the library.
4 No parking.
5 Fasten your seat belt.

b)

1 You can't fish.
2 You have to drive carefully.
3 You can't eat or drink.
4 You can't park.
5 You have to fasten your seat belt.

2a)

1 At school, you can't shout at the
   teachers and you have to do your
   homework.
2 In an art gallery, you can't touch the
   paintings and you have to be quiet.
3 On a road in the UK, you can't break the
   speed limit and you have to drive on the
   left.
4 On an aeroplane, you can't open the
   window and you have to sit down during
   take-off.
5 In the army, you can't stay in bed all day
   and you have to obey orders.

b)

1 On the London Underground you can't
   smoke.
2 In the UK drivers can't drive on the right.
   In France, drivers have to drive on the
   right.
3 In the UK, people can't carry a gun.
   An American police officer has to carry
   a gun.
4 Surgeons have to wash their hands
   before an operation.
   You can wash your hands with or
   without soap.
5 On a motorbike, you have to wear a
   helmet in the UK.
   On a skateboard, you don't have to wear
   a helmet, but it's a good idea.

3a), b) and c) 🎧 (16)

Examples:
The <u>people</u> can <u>see</u> us.
I <u>know</u> they <u>can</u>.✔
 1 Can you <u>see</u> him?
 2 <u>Yes</u>, I <u>can</u>.✔
 3 I <u>can't</u> speak <u>French</u>.✔
 4 I can <u>ride</u> a <u>horse</u>.
 5 What <u>languages</u> can she <u>speak</u>?
 6 They can <u>do</u> what they <u>want</u>.
 7 You <u>can't</u> <u>smoke</u> in the <u>office</u>.✔
 8 I <u>can</u>.✔
 9 <u>No</u>, you <u>can't</u>.✔
10 Can <u>Jenny</u> come <u>too</u>?

4 🎧 (17)

Conversation 1

FATHER: Now hurry up. We haven't got
          much time and you still haven't …
CHILD: Daddy. Why do I have to go to
          school?
FATHER: Because I have to go to work. Now
          come on, eat your breakfast …

Conversation 2

HUSBAND: Is Mark ready yet?
WIFE: He says he doesn't want to wear a
          tie.
H: Well … he doesn't have to wear a
          tie.
W: George! He can't go to a wedding
          in a T-shirt and jeans! I mean he …

Conversation 3

MAN: … and where can you smoke?
WOMAN: You can only smoke in the
          smoking area.
MAN: I see … and where's that exactly … ?

Conversation 4

ATTENDANT: Excuse me! You can't take photos
           in here!
VISITOR: Really? Oh, I'm sorry I didn't …
A: No. You have to leave your
           camera at the entrance.
V: Oh, I see. OK, yeah, I'll …

Conversation 5

TEACHER: OK … right … OK…now your
          homework … listen, listen … Now
          you have to do this homework …
          yes … but you don't have to do it
          this evening … you can give it to
          me next week but you … look,
          please … please listen, listen … I
          only want …

2 a) He doesn't have to wear a tie.
  b) He can't go to a wedding in T-shirt
     and jeans.
3 a) Where can you smoke?
  b) You can only smoke in the smoking
     area.
4 a) You can't take photos there.
  b) You have to leave your camera at the
     entrance.
5 a) You have to do this homework.
  b) You don't have to do it (the
     homework) this evening.

5

1 make   2 let   3 let   4 let   5 make   6 lets
7 makes   8 makes   9 makes   10 lets

6

 3 They don't let us make a lot of noise.
 4 You have to wear a uniform.
 5 They don't let him use the office phone.
 6 They make me clean their cars.
 7 You have to pay before you go in.
 8 They don't let the workers smoke in the
   building.
 9 She can't go home early on Fridays.
10 They have to get up at six o'clock every
   morning.
11 They make you learn Latin and Greek.
12 They don't let me park in front of my
   house.

7

DEREK: I went to Greece last month.
MAEVE: Did you?
D: I don't go abroad very often.
M: Don't you?
D: No, but I like Greece.
M: Do you?
D: Oh yes. The people are so kind.
M: Are they?
D: My wife's Greek, actually.
M: Is she?
D: Yes. We visited her family.
M: Did you?
D: Yes. In fact. She's still there.
M: Is she?
D: Mmm. She didn't come back with me.
M: Didn't she?
D: No. She doesn't want to live in England.
M: Doesn't she?
D: No. She hates the weather.
M: Does she?
D: Yes. So we're going to live in Greece.

M: Are you?

D: Yes. I'm not going to work here any more.

M: Aren't you?

D: No. In fact today is my last day.

M: Good! ... erm ... I mean ... Goodbye .

8

2 = l) Was she? What did she look like?

3 = i) Was she? How is she now?

4 = c) Did you? Where did you go?

5 = g) Weren't you? What was wrong with you?

6 = b) Don't you? Neither do I.

7 = d) Didn't you? So why did you go?

8 = j) Do you? So do I.

9 = a) Is he? Where does he work?

10 = e) Do I? Well, I didn't sleep well last night.

11 = f) Aren't they? Well, I'm going. Are you?

12 = k) Does she? What does she want to do?

6 Where on earth?

1a) b) and c) 〔OO〕 (18)

When I was young, my favourite place was a forest called Sweetwood near my cousins' house. We lived in London, but my parents took my sister and me to see my cousins every summer and every Christmas. They lived in the country so it was really different. The five of us – me, my sister, and my three cousins – spent most of the time in this forest. In winter it was like a different country – all snow and ice and the trees had no leaves. It was like a magic snow castle.

In summer we played wonderful games down there. Sometimes, I walked round alone. I climbed up a very big tree we called "The Emperor" and sat for hours, looking at the sun through the leaves, or watching my cousins and sister playing below. No-one knew I was there. It was fantastic.

I think the thing I remember best is the silence. I mean, we made a lot of noise, but when we stopped, everything stopped. I don't even think there were birds there. The last time I went was last September. It was my uncle's birthday and he had a big party in the garden of their house. I went for a walk in the forest. It's still beautiful, but it's not as big as I remembered it. Even "The Emperor" is small.

a)

Picture c) shows Sweetwood.

b)

1 Twice a year. (Every summer and every Christmas.)

2 His sister and his cousins.

3 Because it was in the country and he lived in London.

4 The silence in the wood.

5 Last September.

2 Example answer:

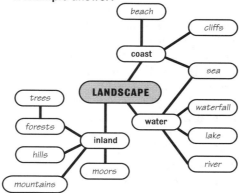

3

1 in / on   2 in   3 on   4 in   5 at   6 on / at   7 in   8 on   9 in (at) / at (on)   10 in

4a)

1 boiling   2 cloudy   3 rain   4 grey skies   5 cold and damp   6 warm   7 mild   8 hot and humid   9 cool   10 blue skies

Bad weather	Good weather
freezing	boiling
cloudy	warm
rain	mild
grey skies	hot and humid
cold and damp	blue skies
cool	

b) 〔OO〕 (19)

And tomorrow's weather ... Starting off in Scotland, where there'll be quite a bit of sun on the east coast, but it will be mainly cloudy and windy over on the west coast. The north of England will be mainly dry with a lot of sun – nice high temperatures there, then, but the temperatures drop as we get nearer London. The south-east will be cold and damp tomorrow with a lot of rain – in fact it'll probably rain for the whole weekend in the south-east. There'll be no rain tomorrow in the south-west, but it will be very cloudy for most of the day. Wales will be wet and rainy for most of the weekend – probably Saturday will be the day when there's most rain in Wales. And finally, good news for those of you living in Northern Ireland – the sun shine all weekend. Tomorrow the sun will come out

and it won't stop until early next week. So, now looking at the international weather map ...

b)

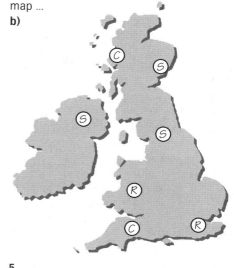

5

1 are   2 is   3 are   4 are   5 Is   6 is   7 Are   8 are   9 is   10 is

6

1 It was   2 There was   3 It is   4 It is   5 There has been   6 There is   7 there is   8 It has been   9 It is   10 There is

7a)

2 = e) I think it will probably rain a lot.

3 = d) We are going to stay in cheap hotels.

4 = f) Perhaps we'll rent a car.

5 = a) No, I don't think so.

6 = b) We'll probably come back on the 26th.

b)

We are going *to*⁽¹⁾ stay in very cheap hotels but John ~~will~~⁽²⁾ is taking a tent because he thinks that we might ~~to~~⁽³⁾ camp outside on one or two nights. I have already told him that I *am*⁽⁴⁾ not going to stay in a tent – if he wants *to*⁽⁵⁾ do it, that's fine, but I am going *to*⁽⁶⁾ stay in a warm bed every night. I think *it*⁽⁷⁾ will probably rain quite a lot, and we will probably ~~be~~⁽⁸⁾ walk for miles every day, so I ~~am~~⁽⁹⁾ think it's important that we ~~to~~⁽¹⁰⁾ get a good night's sleep every night! Anyway, I *am*⁽¹¹⁾ sure John won't want to sleep in a tent. But if he wants *to*⁽¹²⁾ carry a tent around Wales for a week, that's ~~is~~ his decision.

8

1 I'll   2 won't pass   3 I'm going   4 are you going to   5 I'll   6 I'm going to   7 I'll do   8 will probably take off

9

1 Do you know what this word means?

2 Can you tell me where she works?

3 Do you know if the bank is open?

4 Could you tell me what her name is?

5 Do you remember where the car is?
6 Could you tell me if this is the London train?
7 Can you tell me how much this costs?
8 Do you know when the train leaves?

10
2 = d)   3 = a)   4 = e)   5 = c)   6 = h)   7 = f)
8 = b)

11 ⊙⊙ (20)

Conversation A:

PAUL: Excuse me. Could you tell me where the nearest bank is, please?

PASSER BY: The bank … let me see. Yes, you go up this road, turn left and it's on the right. About two minutes' walk.

PAUL: Cheers.

Conversation B:

P: Excuse me. Do you know if there's a post office near here?

PB: A post box?

P: No, a *post office*.

PB: Ah, a post office – yes … now, you go straight up this road, take the first turning on the right, second turning on your left, and there it is, on the right. Just next to the school. *Or* you could go up to the end of this road, turn right, then take the second turning on the right, and it'll be on your left. *Or*… you could always go *down* this road …

P: No, no, that's OK really… Thanks very much.

Conversation C:

P: Excuse me. Where's the nearest pub, please?

FIRST PB: I don't know! I don't drink!

P: Oh … er … ah! … Excuse me! Could you tell me where the nearest pub is, please?

SECOND PB: Sure. Er … the nearest pub is the Red Lion. Erm. Let's see … you go up this road, turn right, turn right again and it's at the very end of that street.

P: Oh … So is it the same if I go *down* this street, turn left at the end, and then the pub will be on my left?

SECOND PB: Erm … yes. I suppose so…

Conversation D:

P: Excuse me. Is there a travel agent's near here?

PB: Yes. It's on this street actually. Just go up this street, and it's at the end on the left.

P: Great. Thanks very much.

PB: No problem.

Conversation E:

P: Excuse me. Erm … could you tell me where the local hospital is, please?

PB: Saint Mary's hospital, you mean?

P: Er … yes, Saint Mary's Hospital.

PB: OK … erm … I think the best way, er … OK … Erm … Go up this road, turn right at the first corner, there, then go along that road to the end and it's on the corner, right opposite the school.

P: Excellent. Thanks very much.

PB: Don't mention it.

11
a) = 5   b) = 4   c) = 1   d) = 3   e) = 2
Building "X" is the school.

Extend your reading Units 5–6

1
1 = F   2 = F   3 = T   4 = F
2
1 = B   2 = D   3 = A   4 = C
3
1 = a)   2 = c)   3 = b)

7 The cruel heart

1a)
b) not marry me / jump
c) not slow down / crash
d) not find the formula / go crazy
e) come closer / scream
b)
b) If you don't marry me, I'll jump!
c) If you don't slow down, you'll crash!
d) If I don't find the formula, I'll go crazy!
e) If you come closer, I'll scream!
c)
b) I'll marry you if you come back inside!
c) Yeah, well, if we crash, I promise I won't ever drink again!
d) But if I find the formula, I'll be the most powerful man in the world!
e) If you scream, nobody will hear you!
d)
b) What will happen if she doesn't marry him?
c) What will happen if she doesn't slow down?
d) What will happen if he doesn't find the formula? He'll go crazy.
e) What will happen if he comes closer? She'll scream.

2a) b) and c) ⊙⊙ (21)
a)
Example: If you <u>need</u> <u>help</u>, I'll <u>help</u> you.
1 If we <u>need</u> <u>advice</u>, we'll <u>ring</u> you.
2 If you <u>don't</u> <u>know</u>, I'll <u>tell</u> you.
3 If you <u>ask</u> <u>Steve</u>, he'll <u>explain</u> it.
4 If you <u>want</u> <u>money</u>, I'll <u>give</u> you <u>some</u>.

b)
Example: Will she <u>come</u> if I <u>ask</u> her?
1 Will they <u>work</u> if he <u>pays</u> them?
2 Will you <u>go</u> if I <u>help</u> you?
3 Will she <u>understand</u> if he <u>tells</u> her?
4 Will he <u>pass</u> if he <u>works</u> <u>hard</u>?

3a)
1
T1: Listen! I think there's someone in the next room.
T2: That's impossible. There isn't anyone in the building at this time of night.
T1: OK. But I'm sure I heard something.
2
P: You must give me something for this cold, doctor!
D: But I have tried everything! I can't think of anything new to give you!
P: In that case, I will have to go somewhere else!
3
T1: I taught that student everything he knows!
T2: But … that student doesn't know anything!
T1: I know, I'm a terrible teacher! Nobody listens to me.
4
G1: I'm going to the kitchen. Does anyone want a cup of tea?
G2: No. I don't want anything, thanks.
G3: Well, I'd like something cold to drink.
G1: I'll look in the fridge. Maybe there's something in there.
5
F: Where did you go last night?
D: I didn't go anywhere. I went to bed, because there was nothing good on TV.
F: Really? Well, someone told me they saw you at *Jimmy's* nightclub.
D: That's impossible. I was at *Frankie's* – I mean … erm …

b)
1 There is no money in this business.
2 He didn't take any risks.
3 We met no interesting people.
4 John doesn't speak any French at all.
5 They had no problems.
6 I haven't heard any news since Sunday.
7 She is making no progress.

4a)
1 fill in   2 travel around   3 pick up
4 grew up   5 think of   6 paid / back
7 look after   8 got up

b)
a) a day off
b) at the moment
c) That's nice of you.
d) next to me

e) halfway through
f) low in calories
g) on my own
1 a day off
2 halfway through
3 That's nice of you.
4 next to me
5 low in calories
6 on my own
7 at the moment
5a)

b)
Food: 1 fattening 2 fizzy 3 delicious
4 fresh 5 tasty
People: 1 handsome 2 successful
3 jealous 4 ruthless 5 famous
6b)
1 The shopping trolley (d) 1937
2 The vacuum cleaner (a) about 1901
3 Sliced bread (c) 1928
4 The motor scooter (b) 1935
c)
1 vacuum cleaner, motor scooter
2 vacuum cleaner, motor scooter
3 a) customers b) enormous
   c) platform d) economical e) bakery
   f) sliced g) chain h) basket
d)
1 T 2 T 3 F 4 F 5 T
7a) and b) 🔊 (22)
Example: <u>interesting</u>.
 1 <u>ad</u>vert
 2 <u>ad</u>vertisement
 3 <u>ad</u>vertise
 4 <u>ad</u>vertising
 5 <u>tel</u>evision
 6 ma<u>ga</u>zine
 7 <u>news</u>paper
 8 con<u>su</u>mer
 9 <u>cus</u>tomer
10 <u>pro</u>duct

8 Future dreams or nightmares?
1a)
1 won't make 2 will destroy 3 will have
4 will want 5 will be 6 will rain
7 will buy 8 will be 9 will sell 10 will be
11 will make 12 will buy
b)
1 Next year we will probably be very poor.
2 We probably won't sell any ice creams.
3 We might lose all our money.
4 We might not eat tonight.
5 I'm sure we'll be unemployed next month.
2 🔊 (23)
1 If you <u>don't</u> listen, you <u>won't</u> understand.
2 If she <u>doesn't</u> try, she <u>won't</u> win.
3 If you <u>haven't</u> got time, then we <u>won't</u>
  have the meeting.
4 You <u>won't</u> succeed if you <u>don't</u> try.
5 I <u>can't</u> explain if you <u>won't</u> let me.
3a), b) and c) 🔊 (24)
INTERVIEWER: So – how do you think the world
          will be different in the future?
          Moira?
MOIRA: I know there are a lot of problems in
     the world, and it's not perfect, but I
     think things are better now than
     they were hundreds of years ago,
     and I really believe that things will
     get better in the future.
     Really. I think people are tired of war
     and fighting, and they just want
     peace. People will try to make peace
     in their small communities because
     they can see that central
     government can't help them.
     Everyone will help their neighbours
     ... I think ...
INT: Hmm. Paul – what do you think?
PAUL: Well. I think Moira's ideas are
    fantastic, and I agree that *some*
    people are fed up with war all the
    time and violence in the streets, but
    I can't see that the situation will get
    better.
    Really, I think things will get more
    violent, there will be more wars. I
    don't think people want peace.
    People want money, and if they need
    a war to get it, then there will be a
    war. Everyone is losing respect for
    everything. And in the future more
    marriages will break down, husbands
    and wives will separate – the child at
    school who has a mother *and* a
    father will be unusual! That is, if
    there *are* schools in the future!
    Education will be more like military
    service I think ...

INT: OK. What about other things? TV,
   fashion, films, literature – that sort
   of thing. Laura?
LAURA: Well I think you can forget literature.
     No-one reads any more. People just
     watch TV or get their information
     from the Internet. In fact, most people
     don't want information!
     They just want to play games! Video
     games, interactive computer
     programmes ... in the future
     everyone will just work and play
     games. No-one will communicate,
     no-one will have conversations,
     no-one will think or have opinions.
     The government will control people
     through television. And fashion?
     No-one will go out with friends
     because it will be too dangerous to
     leave your house, so no-one will
     wear nice clothes. Fashion will die.
     The supermodels will have to get
     real jobs.
INT: Uh uh. Dan – do you agree with Laura?
DAN: Well, no, frankly. I mean more people
    are buying books now than ever
    before. People are reading more, not
    less. You have to read to use the
    Internet.
    In fact, I see computers and the
    Internet as a really good thing. In the
    future people will all communicate on
    the Internet, we'll all make films and
    write books and put them on the
    Internet! Everyone will talk to everyone
    across the world. Listen – people want
    to communicate! Even now in schools
    children are learning to communicate
    their ideas on the Net – they are
    learning a new way to come together
    ... And very soon everyone will have
    really small cameras and they can
    film whatever they want and put it on
    the Internet. Politicians will have no
    control over what we see. We'll all be
    free. And as for fashion – well, Laura,
    people will always wear nice clothes
    because they'll be on TV all the time!
a)
1 Moira – optimistic
  Paul – pessimistic
  Laura – pessimistic
  Dan – optimistic
2 MOIRA: People just want peace.
  PAUL: People want money.
  LAURA: People just want to play games.
  DAN: People want to communicate.

b)
1 Laura and Dan   2 Laura and Dan
3 Moira and Dan   4 Laura   5 Paul
6 Laura   7 Dan   8 Paul and Laura
9 Paul and Dan   10 food, drugs, telephone,
transport

4a)

Regular	Irregular
dangerously	well
badly	fast
slowly	hard
happily	
carefully	

b)
1 hard / well   2 carefully   3 slowly
4 happily   5 fast / dangerously   6 badly

c)
1 quickly / easy   2 calm / nervous
3 cold / patiently   4 efficiently / slow
5 quiet / angry

5a)
1 The man walked towards the car.
2 Jane ran after the dog.
3 They spent two weeks crossing the
   sands of the desert, trying to find some
   sign of civilisation.

b)
The woman closed her eyes and waited for
a moment outside the office building. At
ten to one she walked to the entrance of
the railway station. She took a mirror from
her handbag and looked at her face. When
she put the mirror back, she felt the metal
of the gun in the bag. She walked to
Platform Five where she could see the man
who she knew was Mr James. She took the
gun from her handbag.

1 Outside the office building.
2 On Platform Five.
3 By foot.
4 Mr James.
5 She wanted to shoot Mr James.

Do You remember? Units 5–8

1a)
selfish
elegant
pessimistic
exotic
truthful
changeable
awful
pleasant
optimistic
dramatic

b)
2 selfish   3 elegant   4 pessimistic
5 truthful   6 awful   7 exotic   8 dramatic
9 optimistic   10 pleasant

2
1 Could you tell me where I can put my
   coat?
2 Do you know if there is any more wine?
3 Do you know who that man is?
4 Could you tell me what the time is?
5 Do you know if anyone is sitting here?

3
1 If I see him I'll tell him.
2 He always arrives late.
3 A: I don't like studying English.
   B: Neither do I – it's too difficult.
4 Please don't talk so quickly – I can't
   understand you.
5 Every week my parents make me clean
   my room.
6 She has never been to Italy.
7 A: What is she like?
   B: She's very friendly – I like her.
8 If he passes the exam, I'll be very
   surprised.
9 They won't let me do what I want!
10 He drove so fast that I felt terrible.
11 Can you tell me where Oxford Street is?
12 There are no rules in my office – we
    can wear anything.

4
1 haven't   2 haven't   3 don't have
4 don't have   5 haven't   6 Don't have

Extend your reading Units 7–8

1
The best definition = c)

2
Section 1 title: Chicken Strips (Put More
Sauce In It doesn't mention the chicken
strips themselves.)
Section 2 title: Don't Try This At Home (not
Risky (and Illegal) Business, as it was risky
but not illegal.)

3
1 = T   2 = F   3 = T   4 = T   5 = F

4
1 = c)   2 = b)   3 = a)

Extend your grammar Units 5–8

1
1 no-one who could   2 had to / was
made to   3 let young people drink
4 going to (go to)   5 musn't be / can't be
6 me when you are going to   7 work
harder, you'll / you will   8 dangerously

2
1 in   2 in   3 in   4 on   5 of   6 in
7 for   8 on   9 on   10 in   11 from

3
1 Have you ever tried   2 tried
3 was eating   4 were   5 take   6 trying

Extend your writing Units 5–8

1
The first paragraph describes the
disadvantages of boarding schools. The
second paragraph concentrates on the
advantages.

2
The best introduction is Number 1.
(Number 2 is rather boring. Number 3 is
interesting, but it does not introduce a
composition about boarding schools in
general. It concentrates on a particular
school.)

3
The best conclusion is Number 3. (Number
1 does not include a logical conclusion
based on the information in the text.
Number 2 only repeats the information in
the text and does not include a logical
conclusion.)

9 My place

1
1 friendly   2 traditional
3 comfortable   4 colourful   5 relaxing

2a) and b) 👀 (25)

SHIRLEY:
I don't think it's the only one of its kind in
the world, and I know it's not valuable or
anything, but I've had it for such a long
time … I didn't buy it in New York actually, I
got it in London, when I was a student. I
thought it was funny … I can't imagine how
many cups of tea and coffee I've had out of
it since then. Hundreds? Thousands?

DAVID:
It sounds stupid, but I really believe that it
brings me luck! I've had it for six years and
I carry it in my pocket wherever I go. It
looks like an ordinary coin, but the
interesting thing about it is that both sides
are the same … you see? I don't know if it's
true, but the person who gave it to me told
me that it used to belong to a gambler on
the Mississippi River. He was very wealthy.
He won a lot of money before he died –
thanks to this … I like it because it's so
heavy – not like modern money … it feels
nice in my hand.

SUSAN:
This reminds me of my first visit to the
States when I was twelve. I went to a
summer camp, and the counsellors made
all the girls play baseball. It was great. I
loved catching the ball in this – your hand
didn't hurt because the leather's so hard. It
was a bit uncomfortable to wear in those
days because my hands were so small …

That was … what … seventeen years ago? And it's still like new!

RUBEN:
I always think "I must throw this away," but I never do. I used to have a lot of toys like this when I was a child. I was a big fan of science fiction. I used to watch all the TV series … this isn't from a TV series actually, but it's excellent – look – it walks and moves its arms … it was probably very expensive. I don't know – my aunt gave it to me about twenty years ago …

a)
Shirley = f) Since she was a student.
David = g) For six years.
Susan = e) Since she was twelve.
Ruben = b) For about twenty years.

c)
short – long
serious – funny
poor – wealthy
light – heavy
awful – great
comfortable – uncomfortable
terrible – excellent
cheap – expensive

3
1 have you known   2 has he been
3 has he lived   4 has she been
5 have they worked

4

for …	since …
two days	yesterday
a week	then
ages	1903
a long time	last summer
all his life	my father died
the first six months	I was born
three years	April

5
1 Jason has lived in New York for six months.
2 They have been married since 1991.
3 Steve and Sarah have known each other for ten years.
4 Betty has had a dog since 1998.
5 They have been vegetarians since 1991.
6 Joe has studied French for two months.

6 🔘🔘 (26)
Example: He worked hard.
1 We've lived there for a year. (a)
2 She walked for miles. (b)
3 They changed their money. (b)
4 He watched a lot of TV. (b)
5 We've looked everywhere. (a)
6 You've read the book. (a)

7a) and b) 🔘🔘 (27)
Example: How <u>long</u> have you <u>lived</u> here?
1 How <u>much</u> did it <u>cost</u>?

2 How <u>long</u> was the <u>film</u>?
3 How <u>old</u> is your <u>father</u>?
4 How <u>many</u> did you <u>buy</u>?
5 How <u>long</u> has she <u>worked</u> there?

8b)
1 Where was he born?
2 How long has he been married?
3 When did he get married?
4 What's his wife's name?
5 How many children has he got?
6 When was Mark / his son born?
7 How old is Maria?
8 How long has he worked for Sonya Communications / this company?
9 When did he start working for Sonya Communications / this company?
10 How much does he earn? How much is his current salary?

9a) and b) 🔘🔘 (28)
A: Lamb Enterprises.
B: Hello. Can I speak to John Lamb, please?
A: Who is calling, please?
B: It's Jane Starkey.
A: Can you spell that, please?
B: S – T – A – R – K – E – Y.
A: Hold the line, please.

A: I'm sorry – he's in a meeting, Ms Starkey.
B: Oh. Do you know when he'll be back?
A: I'm afraid not. He has been in the meeting since 9:15.
B: Oh. OK. Can you ask him to call me?
A: Certainly. May I take your number?
B: Yes, sure. It's 456 7890.
A: Right. I'll tell him.
B: Thanks. Goodbye.
A: Goodbye.

10 a) and b) 🔘🔘 (29)
Example: A: Is that two three six, nine one four two?
          B: No. This is two three <u>seven</u>, nine one four two.
1 A: Is that two three six, nine one four two?
  B: No. This is two three six, nine one four <u>three</u>.
2 A: She's gone to Morocco.
  B: <u>Where</u> has she gone?
3 A: Do you want to wait?
  B: No I <u>don't</u> want to wait!
4 A: Is he at work?
  B: No – he's at <u>home</u>.
5 A: He's in a meeting with Miss Love.
  B: <u>Who's</u> he in a meeting with?
6 A: Can he phone you tomorrow?
  B: No – I want to talk to him <u>today</u>.
7 A: The meeting finishes at 6:15.
  B: <u>When</u> does the meeting finish?

11

Down	Across
1 bed	2 shelves
2 stairs	5 drawers
3 vase	6 carpet
4 sink	9 fridge
6 computer	10 pot
7 toilet	11 sheets
8 rug	13 machine
11 sofa	
12 shoe	

10 He loves me, he loves me not …

1
1 in   2 up   3 out   4 out   5 in   6 off   7 out
8 up

2a) and b) 🔘🔘 (30)
Examples: married ✓   divorced ✗
1 separated ✓
2 engaged ✗
3 fancied ✓
4 chatted ✓
5 interested ✓
6 asked ✗
7 invited ✓
8 excited ✓
9 decided ✓
10 wanted ✓
11 bored ✗
12 changed ✗
13 argued ✗
14 depressed ✗

3a)
1 Mary was making a cake.
2 Joy was having a shower.
3 Vince was sleeping.
4 Sally was fixing her car.
5 Trevor was working in the garden.
6 Tony was cleaning the house.

b)
1 What was Sally doing?
2 What were Trevor and Tony doing?
3 What was Vince doing?

4a)
1 = c)   2 = f)   3 = a)   4 = g)   5 = d)   6 = e)
7 = b)

b)
2 Paul was painting the ceiling when he fell off the ladder.
3 The students weren't listening when the teacher explained the exercise.
4 Anne was looking for her passport when she found an old diary.
5 Carla wasn't driving very fast when the police officer stopped her.
6 They were listening to the radio when they heard the news.
7 The shop assistant wasn't looking when I stole the book.

5

1 didn't / weren't   2 Did / was
3 Were / didn't   4 wasn't / was
5 didn't / was   6 weren't / didn't / was

6a) and b) 🎧 **(31)**

Examples: <u>Where</u> was he <u>going</u>?
She was <u>writing</u> a <u>letter</u>.
He <u>wasn't</u> <u>listening</u>

1 <u>What</u> was she <u>doing</u>?
2 They <u>weren't</u> <u>working</u>.
3 He was <u>driving</u> to <u>Scotland</u>.
4 <u>What</u> were you <u>looking</u> at?
5 I was <u>trying</u> to <u>help</u>.
6 She <u>wasn't</u> <u>driving</u>.
7 <u>Why</u> were they <u>crying</u>?
8 <u>Who</u> was she <u>talking</u> to?
9 You were <u>reading</u> a <u>book</u>.
10 <u>How</u> was she <u>feeling</u>?

7

1 = f)   2 = a)   3 = d)   4 = g)   5 = c)
6 = h)   7 = j)   8 = e)   9 = b)   10 = i)
11 = m)   12 = o)   13 = k)   14 = l)   15 = n)

8a)

1 She irritates me.
2 He gets on my nerves.
3 It makes me angry.
4 She drives me crazy.

b)

2 It gets on my nerves when my neighbours have parties.
3 It drives me crazy when companies play music down the phone.
4 It makes me angry when shop assistants ignore me.
5 It gets on my nerves when people at the bus stop don't queue.
6 It irritates me when kids play football outside.
7 It gets on my nerves when people on buses use mobile phones.

c) 🎧 **(32)**

I mean it's impossible. Every night of the week the same thing. Well – not *every* night. Maybe once a month ... but anyway they make so much noise. People arrive at nine in the evening and sometimes they stay until midnight or one in the morning! It's ridiculous. They play that awful "pop" music – why can't they play good music? I could play the piano for them, but they never ask me. In fact, they never even talk to me. Well, they say "Good morning" and "Good evening" and "How are you?" but I don't answer! Oh no! I want them out of the flat as soon as possible. I've told the police. Hundreds of times. They say that I should relax! That's the problem with this country! There's no organisation! No authority! Not like when I was young. When I was young

the police were adults – much older than me! Now they're children! Teenagers! How can you organise a country when the police should still be at school?

c)

1 Picture 2
2 a) = T   b) = F   c) = F   d) = T   e) = T
f) = T

9a)

1 No, it isn't. (It's a daily programme.)
2 No, it didn't. It used to be on at 1:30.
3 When Sharneen died.
4 No, she didn't. (She wanted her to split up with Dan.)
5 In a factory accident.
6 No, he won't. (The writers say something horrible will happen to him.)
7 Yes, it is.

b)

1 was talking / asked
2 laughed / asked
3 got

c)

1 Bongo (M)   2 Kimmie (F)
3 Dr Shane (M)   4 Sparky (M)

Extend your reading Units 9–10

1 £110,000
2 1 = a)   2 = c)   3 = c)   4 = b)   5 = b)
3a) 1 of   2 in / in   3 in   4 for   5 to
b)
1 = T   2 = F (it started in the 1980s)
3 = F (Teddy Girl is the most famous)
4 = F (a Japanese businessman bought Teddy Girl)   5 = T

11 *If ...*

1a)

2 = f) dictionary   3 = a) calculator
4 = e) washing machine   5 = b) umbrella
6 = c) microwave

b) and c)

2 If he had a dictionary, he would understand the word.
3 If she had a calculator, she would know the answer.
4 If he had a washing machine, his clothes wouldn't be dirty.
5 If he had an umbrella, he wouldn't be wet.
6 If they had a microwave, the meat would be ready.

2

1 Well ... if we had a radio, we could listen to (some) music.
2 If we had a lot of money, we could buy a video and a radio.
3 If we had a private jet, we could fly to New York.

4 OK. If we lived near the sea, we could go swimming.
5 Well, Matt. If you had any good ideas, I could agree with you.

3

1 Do people have wings?   Yes ☐   No ☑
  Can they fly?   Yes ☐   No ☑
  If people had wings, they could fly.
2 Does money grow on trees?   Yes ☐   No ☑
  Does it have any value?   Yes ☑   No ☐
  If money grew on trees, it wouldn't have any value.
3 Do we have bones?   Yes ☑   No ☐
  Can we stand up?   Yes ☑   No ☐
  If we didn't have bones, we couldn't stand up.
4 Can most birds fly?   Yes ☑   No ☐
  Do they have to walk everywhere?   Yes ☐   No ☑
  If most birds couldn't fly, they would have to walk everywhere.
5 Is every country exactly the same?   Yes ☐   No ☑
  Do people go abroad on holiday?   Yes ☑   No ☐
  If every country were exactly the same, people wouldn't go abroad on holiday.
6 Can animals talk to us?   Yes ☐   No ☑
  Do we eat meat?   Yes ☑   No ☐
  If animals could talk to us, we wouldn't eat meat.
7 Does everyone speak the same language?   Yes ☐   No ☑
  Do people have to study English?   Yes ☑   No ☐
  If everyone spoke the same language, people wouldn't have to study English.

4a) and b) 🎧 **(33)**

Examples: If he <u>spoke</u> <u>French</u>, he'd <u>work</u> in <u>Paris</u>.
If he <u>didn't</u> speak <u>English</u>, he <u>wouldn't</u> have that <u>job</u>.

1 She'd <u>work</u> for <u>Microsoft</u> if she could <u>program</u> <u>computers</u>.
2 If they <u>didn't</u> have to <u>work</u>, they'd <u>live</u> on the <u>beach</u>.
3 I <u>wouldn't</u> work here if I could <u>do</u> something <u>else</u>.
4 I could <u>go</u> <u>anywhere</u> if I <u>had</u> a lot of <u>money</u>.
5 If I <u>lived</u> in <u>America</u>, I'd <u>live</u> in <u>New</u> <u>York</u>.

c) and d) 🎧 **(34)**

1 I could <u>help</u> you if you <u>let</u> me.
2 He'd <u>come</u> if you <u>asked</u> him.
3 If I could read his <u>writing</u>, I'd <u>understand</u> the <u>letter</u>.

4 If she <u>couldn't</u> play the <u>piano</u>, she
<u>wouldn't</u> be <u>happy</u>.
5 People would be <u>happier</u> if they could <u>fly</u>.

5
Have you thought about:
... borrowing some money?
... looking for work in the USA?
... doing some kind of training course?
Why don't:
... you look through the papers?
... you go and live with your parents?
... you ask your parents for money?
I think:
... you should go on holiday.
... you should move abroad.
... you should join the army.
If I were you:
... I would get a temporary job.
... I would ask for my job back.
... I'd start my own business.

6a) and b)  **(35)**

LULU: Oh, well, I don't know, really. I don't
think you know what you want. Maybe
you should just ask for your job back.

SAM: Oh no. I couldn't do that.

L: OK. Well, have you thought about starting
your own business?

S: Mmm. That's a good idea. But what could
I do?

L: Well, what are you interested in?

S: Music ... drinking ... Hey — I could open
a pub.

L: No. I don't think you should open a pub.

S: Well, what do you think I should do?

L: Well. What about a music shop? I mean,
selling CDs and videos ...

S: Hey. Great idea. I've wanted to work in a
music shop since I was a child. But it'll
be really expensive!

L: Well, you could rob a bank!

S: No, that's too dangerous.

L: Well, borrow money from the bank, then.

S: Yes. I think you're right. Maybe I will. Or
maybe I'll be an astronaut ...

L: Oh, Sam ...

a)
1 take a year off
2 take a part time job
3 start his own business✓
4 move to a different country
5 open a music shop✓
6 rob a bank
7 borrow money from the bank✓
8 do some training

7
1 If I were you, I'd take up a sport.
2 Have you thought about learning
Chinese?
3 I think you should get a divorce.

4 Have you thought about moving house?
5 Why don't you see a doctor?

8
1 What would you do if you had a million
pounds?
2 If I were you, I would leave your job.
3 Have you thought about learning a
language?
4 I would be very happy if she were in
love with me.
5 A: You should give up smoking.
 B: That's a good idea!
6 If we were rich, we wouldn't have to go
to work.
7 If I didn't have my car, I wouldn't be
able to go to work.
8 A: Why don't you phone her?
 B: Oh no. I couldn't do that.
9 Has he thought about looking for
another job?
10 Where would you go if you could go
anywhere in the world?
11 You shouldn't complain so much.
12 If you were right, I wouldn't argue
with you.

9

T	M	U	S	I	C	I	A	N	
R	M	R	K	B	O	A	X	D	
A	L	I	O	P	Y	R	A	I	
V	U	G	N	A	V	C	W	R	
E	T	S	L	I	M	H	A	E	
L	H	P	J	K	S	I	I	C	
A	C	T	O	R	A	T	T	T	
G	Y	E	O	P	G	E	E	O	
E	L	V	K	M	E	C	R	R	
N	Q	U	G	O	N	T	B	D	
T	S	T	U	N	T	M	A	N	

1 travel agent 2 musician 3 architect
4 actor 5 director 6 Minister 7 agent
8 stuntman 9 waiter 10 play

12 Love me, love my car
1a) and b)  **(36)**

INTERVIEWER: What car would you have if you
could have any car in the world?
Janice ...?

JANICE: It's easier to tell you what I wouldn't
have. I hate cars like Porsches and
Ferraris — status symbols. But you
know ... I'd love to drive a really old
car — I mean really old — vintage.
Something from 1910 or 1920. I
know they're really slow and

probably very unsafe, but they look
so elegant.

INT: What about you, Mandy?

MANDY: I would have *any* car in the world!
As long as it was cheap. My present
car is getting really old now. I'm
probably risking my life every time I
take it on the road. It's time for a
change. I'm tired of being cold and
uncomfortable when I drive. Frankly
any car would be better — and
probably safer — than my old thing.

INT: Tim?

TIM: It wouldn't really matter which car I
bought, but it would have to be
expensive — a Rolls Royce maybe. I
want something big and comfortable
— maybe with a chauffeur! I want
people to think "There goes
someone who's a success!".

INT: And you, David?

DAVID: I'd have a big four-wheel drive thing.
That way I'd feel safe whenever I
drove — I'd be above all the other
drivers. It would be like driving a
tank, but much faster. In fact, I
might even get it in green — you
know, that sort of military green.

a)
What car would you have if you could have
any car in the world?
Janice = b) Mandy = a) Tim = f)
David = e)
b)
1 Mandy and Tim 2 Mandy 3 Tim
4 Janice and David 5 Mandy and Tim
6 David

2
1 passenger 2 driver 3 mirror
4 windscreen wiper 5 seat belt
6 steering wheel 7 police officer
8 road sign 9 driving licence
10 headlights

3a) and b)  **(37)**
<u>pop</u>ular
cre<u>a</u>tive
<u>beau</u>tiful
re<u>lax</u>ing
<u>dif</u>ferent
am<u>bi</u>tious
<u>glam</u>orous
un<u>hap</u>py
ef<u>fic</u>ient
<u>terr</u>ible
ro<u>man</u>tic
un<u>ti</u>dy
suc<u>cess</u>ful
un<u>faith</u>ful
<u>won</u>derful

welcoming
passionate
colourful
attractive

Ooo	oOo
popular	creative
beautiful	relaxing
different	ambitious
glamorous	unhappy
terrible	efficient
wonderful	romantic
welcoming	untidy
passionate	successful
colourful	unfaithful
	attractive

4
Gemini: lively
Cancer: moody
Pisces: creative
Leo: proud
Virgo: tidy
Taurus: traditional
Libra: cautious
Aries: jealous
Scorpio: passionate
Aquarius: pessimistic
Sagittarius: independent

5a)
3 "Sorry. Can you repeat the question, please, Sir?"
4 "Open your bag!"
5 "Can you make some coffee, darling?"
6 "Don't cross the road here."

b)
3 The boy asked the teacher to repeat the question.
4 The customs officer told him to open his bag.
5 She asked her husband to make some coffee.
6 She told her son not to cross there.

6a) and b) ⊙⊙ (38)
Examples: She <u>told</u> me to <u>hurry</u>.
           Did they <u>ask</u> him <u>not</u> to <u>speak</u>?
1 She <u>told</u> me to <u>leave</u>.
2 Did he <u>tell</u> her <u>not</u> to <u>go</u>?
3 They <u>asked</u> him to <u>stay</u>.

4 They <u>told</u> me to <u>stop</u> it.
5 Did he <u>ask</u> you to <u>read</u> it?

7
1 She asked them not to tell anyone.
2 He told her to slow down.
3 He told her not to drive so fast.
4 She asked them to sign the form.
5 They told her to get out of there.
6 He asked her to marry him.

7 She asked him not to turn the TV on.
8 He told him to shut up.

Do you remember? Units 9–12
1
1 A: How long has she lived there?
  B: Since last summer, I think.
2 I have only known her for three weeks.
3 I haven't had a holiday since 1966.
4 A: Have you seen Jane recently?
  B: No. No-one has seen her for ages.
5 A: Tom has been terribly depressed since he lost his job.
  B: I know. He hasn't spoken to anyone for weeks!

2
1 left   2 wanted   3 was walking   4 met
5 was going   6 decided   7 arrived
8 were arguing   9 came   10 bought

3
1 A: If she loved me, I would be so happy.
  B: Why don't you ask her out?
2 A: If I knew what was wrong, I would feel more relaxed.
  B: I think you should go to a doctor.
3 A: I would get a better job if I had better qualifications.
  B: If I were you, I would study at an evening school.
4 A: If I didn't smoke, I wouldn't have this terrible cough.
  B: Have you thought about giving up?

4a) and b) ⊙⊙ (39)
A: Hello?
B: Hello. This is Dan Holmes. Is that Springfield Records?
A: No, I'm afraid not. You've got the wrong number.
B: Oh – I'm very sorry.
A: That's OK. Goodbye.

A: Hello. Springfield Records.
B: Hi. This is Dan Holmes.
A: How do you spell that, please?
B: H – O – L – M – E – S. Can I speak to Terry, please?
A: Certainly. Hold the line, please.

Extend your reading Units 11–12
1
1 Ricky became interested in cars when he was a boy and his friend Jack let him drive his car.
2 Rock 'n' Roll and Country music.
3 He fixes and restores them. He keeps them in his junkyard on his farm.

2
car parts: clutch, steering wheel, 4-speed engine

actions: fixing up, to drive around, worked on, restored
places: junkyard, property, fields
makes of car: Fairlane, Chevrolet, Ford, Cadillac

3 1 = F   2 = T   3 = T   4 = T   5 = T

4
Chuck couldn't believe Ricky was saving those terrible old cars – he probably thought Ricky was either crazy or stupid.

Extend your grammar Units 9–12
1
1 reading   2 have   3 to   4 me
5 intelligent   6 so   7 for   8 much
9 might   10 going   11 would
12 driving   13 was   14 down
15 haven't

2
1 had this watch for   2 have a computer, so   3 have to get up early.   4 you, I would /'d throw away   5 me to fill in a / the / that

3
going to have; should; will fall; am going; have been; break up; meet

Extend your writing Units 9–12
1
Shona thinks she is in love with a man from New Zealand. He will go back to his country soon and she is afraid she will be unhappy. She doesn't know if she should tell him that she loves him, or not.

2
1 No.
2 Yes (including your address makes things easier for the other person when he/she writes back).
3 No (you only do this in formal letters).
4 After her address.
5 She used the words *Dear Kim*.
6 She put a comma after Kim's name.
7 She wrote *Love* and signed her name.

3 Model answer

> Dunge Farm
> Goodfield
> Derbyshire
> DY12 9TS
>
> 25th May 2000
>
> Dear Shona,
>
> Thank you for your last letter. It was good to hear from you so soon.
>
> You ask me about my new life. Well, we are very happy here. It's true that we are a long way from civilization, but life is simple and the air is clean! It's certainly a good change.
>
> Now, about your love life. Why do you always do same thing? Can't you find a normal man? I think you should take a chance and tell him you love him. If I were you, I'd enjoy the few weeks that he's there with you and I wouldn't worry about the future. And if he loves you too, why don't you ask him to stay?
>
> Write back soon and tell me all about it.
>
> Love,
>
> Kim

13 What a holiday!

1

1 is 2 is 3 are 4 are 5 is
6 is 7 is 8 is 9 are 10 is
11 is 12 is 13 Are 14 is 15 is

2a) and b) 🔾🔾 (40)

Example:

road   1 (sport)   2 aerobics
broken   word   careful
coach   world   stairs
(board)   person   (are)
coast   surfing   airport

3 wave   4 water   5 couple
  break   thought   (group)
  (speak)   awful   hurry
  straight taught   customer
  complaint (show)   public

6 sign   7 cruise
  blinds   (build)
  sights   suit
  (ring)   fruit
  private   juice

3a)

1 Have you done a painting class yet?
2 Have you been horse-riding yet?
3 Have you done an aerobics class yet?
4 Have you played tennis yet?
5 Have you been jet skiing yet?

b)

1 Yes, I have. I went to a painting class on Tuesday.
2 No. Not yet.
3 Yes, I have. I did an aerobics class on Monday and Wednesday.
4 Yes, I have. I played tennis on Wednesday.
5 No. Not yet.

4

1 How long 2 How many 3 How much
4 How long 5 How many 6 How much
7 How long 8 How many 9 How much
10 How long

5

1 It's going to rain.
2 He's going to die.
3 He isn't going to get the job.
4 She's going to get a divorce.
5 He isn't going to pass the exam.

6a)

(A) location	(B) movement	movement – opposite to (B)
in	into	out of
on	onto	off

b)

1 in 2 on 3 out of 4 off 5 into 6 onto

7a)

b) 1 He has put on his coat.
   2 He is putting on his hat.
   3 He is going to leave the house.
c) 1 They have eaten a big meal.
   2 They are smoking cigars.
   3 They are going to pay the bill.
d) 1 She has packed her cases.
   2 She is phoning for a taxi.
   3 She is going to go to the airport.
e) 1 They have drunk too much.
   2 They are driving too fast.
   3 They are going to crash.
f) 1 She has had a shower.
   2 She is putting on make-up.
   3 She is going to get dressed.

b)

b) He hasn't left the house yet.
c) They haven't paid the bill yet.
d) She hasn't gone to the airport yet.
e) They haven't crashed yet.
f) She hasn't got dressed yet.

8a) 🔾🔾 (41)

Conversation 1

CUSTOMER: But I only bought this shirt this morning.

SHOP ASSISTANT: Well, I don't know that. You haven't got a receipt.

C: I know, but you sold it to me! You must remember. It was only a few hours ago.

SA: I've never seen you before ...

Conversation 2

STATION WORKER: I'm sorry, but you have to buy your ticket from the machine.

CUSTOMER: But the machine doesn't work! That's why I'm talking to you!

SW: I can't do anything. I can't sell you a ticket. All tickets from the machine.

C: But the machine doesn't work! I'm going to miss my train ...

a)

Who?	Where?	What about?
customer and shop assistant	in a shop	a shirt
station worker and customer	at a railway station	buying a ticket

b) and c) 🔾🔾 (42)

CUSTOMER: Excuse me ...

MECHANIC: Yes, what can I do for you?

C: I've come for my car. You said I should come in on Friday.

M: But it's only Tuesday.

C: No – last Friday. Five days ago. It's a blue Volkswagen Beetle. Is it ready yet?

M: Oh dear. No, no, no. Erm, that won't be ready until next week. Maybe the week after. It's a very difficult job.

C: But you only had to fix the door on the passenger side, because I couldn't open it.

M: Ah yes, but your car needs a new door. In fact, it needs two new doors. And ... erm ... some other things. And all the parts come from Mexico.

C: Mexico? But it's a German car. Can't you get them in Germany?

M: Not for your car. Mexico.

C: How long is all this going to take?

M: Well, as I say, it could be two weeks, erm, it could be a month.

C: Oh, forget it. Just give me my car back.

M: I can't.

C: Why not?

M: It hasn't got any doors. Or wheels. I am in the middle of repairing it. You'll have to wait. But you can pay me now if you want to.

C: But you haven't finished the job. How do you know how much it'll cost?

M: I'm a professional. I always know how much a job is going to cost, because I can see what the problem is.

C: And the problem here is that you're buying car doors and car wheels in Mexico.

M: Exactly.

c: This is ridiculous. Let me speak to the manager.

M: You are speaking to the manager.

c: I'll phone you next month.

M: OK ... or the month after ...

b)
1 = C 2 = M 3 = C 4 = C 5 = M 6 =M

c)
1 = F 2 = T 3 = T 4 = F 5 = T 6 = T
7 = T

9

Across	Down
1 stairs	1 surfing
4 help	2 away
6 mini-bar	3 some
9 fly	5 paragliding
11 diving	7 noisy
13 guests	8 blind
15 luggage	10 jet
17 ski	12 me
19 conditioning	14 sights
21 to	15 lock
	16 gone
	17 suit
	18 hot
	20 no

14 Crime doesn't pay!

1

1 a) A burglar steals money / jewellery / televisions / wallets / silver.
  b) A burglar robs houses / flats.
2 a) A pickpocket steals wallets / money / jewellery.
  b) A pickpocket robs people.
3 a) A bank robber steals money / jewellery / silver.
  b) A bank robber robs banks.

2a)

She / He's got ...

a small nose
a round face
dark skin
short hair
long fingers
grey eyes
small hands

She / He's ...

tall
in his / her thirties
fit
middle-aged
about 26
thin
quite short

She / He's wearing ...

blue trousers
jeans
make-up
a suit
some jewellery
glasses
a dress

2b) 👓 (43)

POLICEWOMAN: So – was he tall? Short?

WITNESS: Normal really.

PW: Did he have long hair? Short hair?

W: Yes.

PW: Which?

W: Both – I mean he had sort of medium hair. It was blonde. Oh – and he had a beard, which was strange because he didn't have a moustache.

PW: OK. I see. What was he wearing?

W: Dark trousers and a white shirt.

PW: A T-shirt?

W: No. A normal shirt. And, erm, he was carrying a jacket. It might have been part of a suit.

PW: How old was he?

W: About fifty? He didn't look young because he was a bit fat ... I don't know. I wasn't wearing my glasses.

b)
The witness is describing the person in picture c).

3a)

b) I've been mugged.
c) My house has been burgled again!
d) The bank has been robbed!
e) All our computers have been stolen.
f) My wallet has been stolen.

b)

b) Where were you mugged? Have you ever been mugged before?
c) When was your house burgled? How many times has it been burgled?
d) When was the bank robbed?
e) But ... How were they stolen?
f) When was your wallet stolen?

c)

b) "Has anybody seen the mugger?"
  "I'm sorry, sir. The mugger hasn't been seen yet."
c) "Have you caught the burglar?"
  "I'm sorry, madam. The burglar hasn't been caught yet."
d) "Have you questioned any witnesses?"
  'Yes! Three witnesses have been questioned."
e) "Have you found the computers?"
  "Yes. All the computers have been found."
f) "Have you arrested the thief?"
  "I'm sorry, sir. The thief hasn't been arrested yet."

4

1 Banks are robbed every day.
2 Someone stole my bicycle last night.
3 Every law has been broken.
4 The police never found the murderer.
5 That law was made 200 years ago.
6 The police arrest people every day.
7 The house was watched all night.
8 Someone has seen the killer!

5a) and b) 👓 (44)

Which word is stressed in these sentences?

1 He was <u>mugged</u>.
2 They were <u>robbed</u>.
3 Was he <u>killed</u>?
4 Were they <u>hurt</u>?

Which two words are stressed in these sentences?

1 <u>When</u> was this <u>done</u>?
2 Has <u>this</u> been <u>checked</u>?
3 <u>Who</u> was <u>killed</u>?
4 <u>Yes</u>, they <u>were</u>.

Which three words are stressed in these sentences?

1 <u>John</u> was <u>arrested</u> on <u>Saturday</u>.
2 <u>How</u> can it be <u>finished</u> so <u>quickly</u>?
3 <u>Sandy</u> was <u>attacked</u> and <u>robbed</u>.

6

1 has 2 has been 3 has been 4 has
5 has been 6 has been 7 has been
8 has 9 has 10 has been

7a)

1 in 2 in 3 in 4 to 5 at 6 by 7 in

b)

1 Because her books have been translated into more languages than those of any other writer.
2 At home.

c) and d) 👓 (45)

During the First World War, Agatha worked in a hospital, where she learned all the information about poisons which she used in her books later. In 1914 she <u>married</u> Archibald Christie. It seems they were happy for a long time, but in 1926 Archie told her that he loved another woman and he <u>wanted</u> to leave her. Soon after that, Agatha disappeared. Her empty car was found. Was she dead? Did she kill herself? Or did someone murder her? Police asked thousands of people to help them find her.

e)

1 About twenty-three years old.
2 Twelve years.
3 Her parents taught her.
  Somebody found her empty car.
  The police asked people to help.

f)

1 memory 2 After that 3 met 4 During
5 successful 6 until

g)

1 Where was she found?

2 Who did she meet in the Middle East?

3 When did she marry him?

4 When did she work in a hospital?

5 How old was she when she died?

Extend your reading Units 13–14

1

Expedition Titanic offers people the opportunity to see the Titanic under the sea. The trip includes a cruise, lectures and instruction sessions and an underwater excursion to see the wreck.

2

1 The Titanic sank.

2 No, there will be a limited number.

3 Nothing will be taken.

4 You can be disqualified and you can't then participate.

3

1 = e)   2 = b)   3 = d)   4 = c)   5 = a)

4

1 = e)   2 = b)   3 = a)   4 = f)   5 = c   6 = d

7 = h)   8 = g)

15 What are you talking about?

1

1 One that isn't very expensive.

2 Give me the one with the chocolate on top.

3 The ones I wore at Julia's wedding.

4 No – I don't think he's got one.

5 Ones with happy endings!

2

1 which   2 who   3 which   4 which   5 who

6 which   7 who   8 who   9 who   10 which

3

1 The one which I lent (to) you last week.

2 The ones which we'll do next July.

3 The one which has all the accounts information on it.

4 The one who introduced the new tax.

5 The ones which you bought yesterday.

4

1 scissors   2 witness   3 guests

4 murderer   5 thief   6 pencil   7 actress

Central column = student

Suggested definition: A student is a person / someone who studies.

5a)

2 = Beethoven   3 = Billie Holiday

4 = Amy Johnson   5 = Marie Curie

6 = Picasso

b)

2 Beethoven was the man who composed *The Eroica Symphony.*

3 Billie Holiday was the woman who sang *Strange Fruit.*

4 Amy Johnson was the woman who flew solo to Australia in 1930.

5 Marie Curie was the woman who discovered radium.

6 Picasso was the man who painted *Guernica.*

6a) and b) 〔◉◉〕 (46)

	/ðæt/	/ðət/
Examples: I didn't know that!	✔	
I didn't know that you were French.		✔
1 The man that stole the money escaped.		✔
2 Who said that?	✔	
3 That doesn't matter.	✔	
4 This one or that one?	✔	
5 This is the school that I went to.		✔
6 I went to that school.	✔	
7 Don't do that!	✔	
8 I'm sure that he knows.		✔
9 I hate that sort of film.	✔	
10 Are these the glasses that you lost?		✔

7

1 She looks angry.

She looks like Hillary Clinton.

She's got blonde hair.

2 He looks dangerous.

He looks like Robert de Niro.

He's got short black hair.

They look sad.

They look like twins.

They've got long black hair.

8a) and b)

1 = i)   A key is a thing you use to open a door.

2 = g)   Shampoo is stuff you wash your hair with.

3 = f)   Paperclips are things which keep papers together.

4 = c)   A thermometer is a thing which takes your temperature.

5 = e)   Vitamin pills are things you take to feel healthier.

6 = j)   Fly spray is stuff which kills flies.

7 = a)   A towel is a thing you use to dry yourself.

8 = h)   Toothpaste is stuff you use to clean your teeth.

9 = d)   Glasses are things you wear to see better.

10 = b)   Olive oil is stuff you use to cook with.

c)

Suggested answers:

1 A diary is a thing you write your appointments in.

2 Suntan lotion is stuff you put on to protect your skin from the sun.

3 A mobile phone is a thing you use to talk to your friends.

4 Gloves are things you put on your hands to keep them warm.

9a), b), c) and d) 〔◉◉〕 (47)

STEVEN: Hi ... you're Jane, aren't you? Jane Farley?

JANE: Yes ... and you're ... erm ... don't tell me ... oh ...

S: Steven. Steven Moore.

J: Right! Steven! Of course. How are you?

S: Fine. When did you arrive?

J: A few minutes ago. How long have you been here?

S: Oh. About an hour. It's incredible. Everyone looks so different. We all look like our parents.

J: I know. I can't recognise anyone.

S: Well – I'm sure you recognise him. All the girls used to love him.

J: Oh my God! Is that Gary Carter? He used to have such lovely long black hair! Now he hasn't got any hair!

S: I know! He works in the local bank. We all thought he would become a famous footballer. Remember?

J: Yeah – I can't believe it. We all look so different – how did you recognise me?

S: I ... I don't know. I knew I'd recognise you ... I mean ... erm ... you look the same. Really ... You haven't changed. ... I mean look at Elizabeth Pike over there. She used to be huge, like a balloon!

J: That's right! Ooh! And look over there! Michael Dobson. He looks OK.

S: Michael Dobson – is he the one who used to go out with Louise Morris?

J: Yes. That's right ... I always thought he was a bit ...

S: Rude? Unfriendly? Stupid?

J: No – not rude exactly ... but sort of quiet and sad ...

S: Moody?

J: Yes. But I liked him.

S: I hated him. Just because he loved sports he used to be horrible to the ones who were bad at sports – like me.

J: Mmm ... I think I'll just go and say hello ... for a minute. I'll be back in a second.

S: Right. Sure.

a)

Jane Farley

Steven Moore

Gary Carter

Elizabeth Pike

Michael Dobson
Louise Morris
b)
1 = F 2 = T 3 = F 4 = F 5 = T 6 = F 7 = F
Good at sport: Gary✓ Michael✓ Steven
10
1 What does he look like?
2 Where does he live?
3 What does he do?
4 What time / When does he get up?
5 What does he wear (for work)?
6 Which languages does he speak?
7 How much does he earn?
8 How many children does he have?
9 What is he like?
10 What does *generous* mean?

16 The strangest thing happened to me …
1
1 tell 2 saying 3 told 4 said 5 say
6 tell 7 told 8 say 9 said 10 Tell
2
2 = c) 3 = b) 4 = a) 5 = d) 6 = i) 7 = j)
8 = f) 9 = g) 10 = h)
3
1 She said (that) he didn't work in that company.
2 "He writes to me every week."
3 "Mark still lives in France."
4 They said (that) they were leaving the next day.
5 They said (that) their house was the one next to the shop.
6 "I love this kind of book."
7 He said that his sister didn't want to go.
8 "Julian doesn't know the answer."
9 She said that she often went there on Saturdays.
10 "I'm not ready."

4a) ◉◉ (48)
JIMMY: So, Bloop, my friend. Where do you come from?
BLOOP: I come from Planet Ditko.
J: That's lovely. And how long does the journey take?
B: It takes four earth-minutes.
J: That's incredible! Do you travel in a flying saucer?
B: We travel by a method you cannot understand.
J: Super. And where are you staying?
B: We are staying with your Prime Minister.
J: Great. A lovely person. And how long are you staying on earth?
B: We're staying until your planet is destroyed!
J: Oh dear!

b)
Jimmy asked Bloop how long the journey took.
Bloop told Jimmy (that) it took four earth-minutes.
Jimmy asked Bloop if he / they travelled in a flying saucer.
Bloop told Jimmy (that) they travelled by a method he couldn't understand.
Jimmy asked Bloop where he was / they were staying.
Bloop told Jimmy (that) they were staying with his / the Prime Minister.
Jimmy asked Bloop how long he was / they were staying on earth.
Bloop told Jimmy (that) they were staying until his / the planet was destroyed.
5
1 so 2 such a 3 so 4 such 5 so
6 such 7 so 8 such a 9 so 10 such an
6a) and b) ◉◉ (49)

		/eɪ/(day)	/iː/(see)	/aɪ/(try)
1	mon**ey**		✓	
2	m**i**nd			✓
3	ch**i**ld			✓
4	del**ay**	✓		
5	bel**ie**ve		✓	
6	pl**ay**ed	✓		
7	cr**i**me			✓
8	compl**ai**n	✓		
9	rec**ei**pt		✓	
10	incr**ea**se		✓	

Do you remember? Units 13–16
1a)
1 Yes, he has. He cleaned them on Monday afternoon.
2 Yes, he has. He repaired it on Tuesday morning.
3 No, not yet. He's going to fix it on Saturday afternoon.
4 No, not yet. He's going to collect it on Saturday morning.
5 No, not yet. He's going to have a day off on Sunday.
b)
1 Has he changed the curtains in Room 307?
2 Has he bought the paint for the reception area?
3 Has he taken the car to the garage?
4 Has he painted the reception area?
5 Has he cut the grass?

Test your English!
1a)
1 = a 2 = v 3 = e 4 = y 5 = o 6 = u
7 = d 8 = o 9 = n 10 = e 11 = a 12 = l
13 = l 14 = t 15 = h 16 = e 17 = e

18 = x 19 = e 20 = r 21 = c 22 = i
23 = s 24 = e 25 = s
b)
Have you done all the exercises?

Extend your reading (Units 15–16)
1
Kevin Sharpe claimed he was at home, except when he walked the dog. A neighbour saw a man with a dog outside his flat, but he didn't clearly see who it was. A pizza man delivered a pizza, but there was no signature to prove it. Mrs Lattice heard the sound of the TV in the evening, and Kevin claimed he watched a film at home, but his neighbour only heard the sound of the TV – it doesn't prove he was there.
2
Finally Kevin confessed. He said that he had planned everything after breaking up with Heather. He called the dog sitter's agency and asked for somebody to look after his dog the evening he killed Heather. Kevin said that he went home to meet the dog sitter and ordered a pizza for the dog sitter. Then he went to Heather's flat. He explained that he had asked her to open the door until she finally invited him to come in. He said that he put some sleeping tablets in the dog's food while Heather wasn't looking. After that, he took a kitchen knife – he knew where to find one –, and killed Heather.
Meanwhile, the dog sitter had taken care of Kevin's dog. The dog sitter said that he walked the dog and kept it from other dogs and people because Kevin had told him that it could get very violent. Finally, he watched TV. Kevin came back home the next morning and the dog sitter left.
3
1 "I walked my dog at around 8 p.m."
2 "I went to sleep after the TV film."
3 "I saw someone with a big dog."

Extend your grammar Units 13–16
1
1 during 2 at 3 talking 4 jealous 5 next
6 was 7 badly 8 until 9 up 10 by
11 questioned 12 explained 13 so
14 later 15 home
2
1 thief who has recently stolen 2 was broken into 3 the dictionary (that/which) Betty 4 such an interesting 5 this jumper washed 6 because she only weighs 7 she just loved California
8 I'm leaving tomorrow

Extend your writing Units 13–16

1

Mr Carver took part in Expedition Titanic and had several problems: he had to wait for the ship in the rain and he fell into the water when he was getting in the submersible. As a result, he was ill.

2

1 No.
2 Yes.
3 Yes.
4 After the second address.
5 He started the letter *Dear Sir / Madam* (without a comma*).
6 With *Yours faithfully,* his signature and his printed name.
*Note: In formal / business letters it is common nowadays not to put any punctuation after expressions such as "Dear *Sir / Madam*" or "Yours faithfully".

3 Model answer

> 29, Hillside St
> Hertford
> HT 8 4QP
>
> Dream Travels
> 23 Deacon St
> Leedington
>
> 28th August 2000
>
> Dear Sir / Madam
>
> I have just returned from my holiday at the Crystal Sea hotel and it has been very disappointing. The rooms at the hotel and the service were terrible.
>
> First, when we arrived at the hotel, my husband and I had to wait at reception for 45 minutes because there was no room for us. Then, our room didn't have a view, as we had requested, and it was also smaller than the one in the brochure. Finally, my husband got sick the second day of the holiday after eating a meal at the hotel. Our holiday was completely ruined.
>
> I think you are responsible for the poor quality of the service, catering and rooms at the Crystal Sea Hotel. Consequently, I demand a full refund of the money I paid. If I don't receive a satisfactory reply within two weeks, I will have to take legal action.
>
> Yours faithfully
>
> *Marion Smith-Waters*
>
> Marion Smith-Waters

Pearson Education Limited,
Edinburgh Gate
Harlow
Essex CM20 2JE
England
and Associated Companies throughout the World.

First published 2000

Set in 11.5/13pt Bulldog

Printed in Chile
by Antartica Quebecor S.A.

ISBN 0 582 30547 0

Illustrated by: Matt Buckley (Chrome-Dome Design), Phil Healey, Tim Kahane, Kim Smith (Eastwing).

Cover illustration by Tim Kahane.

Acknowledgements

The publishers are most appreciative of the contribution of Ana Fraile and Alejandro Zarzalejos as authors of the 'Extend your reading/ grammar/writing' pages in this Workbook and wish to thank them. The publishers would also particularly like to thank Frances Banks (freelance Editor) for her contribution to the development of the manuscript and the editing of this Workbook.

Photo Acknowledgements

We are grateful to the following for permission to reproduce copyright photographs:

Ronald Grant Archive for 13; Hulton Getty for 33 (a,b,d), 43, 68, 71(a, c, d, e, f); Pearson Education/Peter Lake for 35; Ann Ronan Picture Library for 71(b) and Tony Stone Images for 33(c).

We are grateful to The Bell Language School, Saffron Walden for their help with the commissioned photograph.

Picture research credit: Nathan Grainger for Image Select International, London.

The back cover photograph of the author by Charles Yacoub.

We are grateful to the following for permission to reproduce copyright material:

About.com, Inc. for an adapted and abridged extract from 'The Mystique of Java' from Internet: http:goeasia.about.com/library/weekly/mcurrent; EMAP International for an adapted extract from 'Tele-Star' April 3-9, 1999, from http:/www.harrison-ford.net/articles/Tele%20star; Penguin Books Ltd for an extract from *Forrest Gump* by Winston Groom; Ricky Van Shelton Inc for an adapted extract from the Ricky Van Shelton Website: http://www.rickyvanshelton.com.